MAGNETIC AMPLIFIERS

Theory and Application

MAGNETIC AMPLIFIERS

Theory and Application

SIDNEY PLATT

Director of Engineering Research and Development
Warner, Incorporated

PRENTICE-HALL, INC.
Englewood Cliffs, N. J.

Library of Congress Catalog Card Number: 58–11838

First printing ....October, 1958
Second printing ....January, 1960
Third printing ....February, 1962
Fourth printing ....June, 1964

Preface

Within a relatively short period of time, the magnetic amplifier has assumed a role of prime importance as a valuable and helpful tool of industry. Its adaptability and versatility, and its present and potential applications, have combined to assure it a bright future.

This book summarizes the history and development of the magnetic amplifier from its origin as a simple saturable-core reactor device to the sophisticated feedback amplifier of the present date. Basic magnetic theory is discussed rather briefly; the operation of the saturable reactor and the magnetic amplifier is described in full detail. The text presents scores of industrial and commercial applications and examines future uses of the magnetic device.

Chapters 1 through 3 of this volume provide an introduction to, and history of, the magnetic amplifier and offer a review of the elements of magnetism, electromagnetism, and electromagnetic induction. Chapter 4 describes the basic saturable reactor, and a large number of applications of the fundamental reactor are covered in Chapter 5. The primary magnetic amplifier, in its non-feedback state, is treated in Chapter 6, and applications of this unit are discussed in Chapter 7. Chapters 8 and 9 describe the effects of external and internal feedback on magnetic amplifiers, with respect to the operation and application of the devices. Additional applications of the magnetic amplifier are described in Chapters 10 through 12; properties and characteristics of the amplifier follow in Chapter 13.

This book is intended for the undergraduate and graduate student in electrical and electronic engineering, and as a source of reference data for the practicing engineer, teacher, and technician. The material is so organized that the student, engineer, or technician, starting at the beginning of the book and continuing through to the end, will gain a comprehensive knowledge of the existing magnetic amplifier art.

Many of the circuits illustrated in this text are patented. Consequently the reader must note that no commercial use of any circuit contained herein should be made without obtaining prior approval from the patent holder. No responsibility is assumed by the author or the publisher for any infringement of patent or other rights of third parties which may result from the use of circuits, systems, or processes described or referred to in this volume.

The author wishes to thank the manufacturers represented in this book for their assistance in supplying circuit schematics and data. The author also wishes to acknowledge the aid and assistance offered by the members of his family during the time in which this book was conceived and written.

SIDNEY PLATT

August 1958
Malverne, N. Y.

Contents

1. Introduction and history   1

1-1. Introduction 1
1-2. Fundamentals of operation 2
1-3. Control characteristics of magnetic amplifiers 4
1-4. History of magnetic amplifiers 6
1-5. Significant patents in the magnetic amplifier art . . 7

2. Elements of magnetism   17

2-1. Introduction 17
2-2. History of magnetism 18
2-3. Magnetic poles 19
2-4. Attraction and repulsion of magnets; Coulomb's law . 20
2-5. The magnetic field 21
2-6. The earth's magnetic field 22
2-7. Classification of magnetic materials 22
2-8. Introduction to magnetic theory 24

3. Electromagnetism and electromagnetic induction   30

3-1. Magnetic effects of current 30
3-2. Magnetic field about a solenoid 32
3-3. The magnetic circuit and magnetic terminology . . 33
3-4. Magnetic units 36
3-5. The magnetic and electric circuits 36
3-6. The magnetization, or B-H curve 37
3-7. Hysteresis 39
3-8. Power losses in ferromagnetic cores 42
3-9. Electromagnetic induction, Faraday's experiments . . 46
3-10. Direction of induced electromotive force, Lenz's law . 47
3-11. Self-induction and inductance 48

3-12. Inductive reactance 50
3-13. Mutual induction 51

4. The saturable reactor   54

4-1. General 54
4-2. Introduction to the saturable reactor. 54
4-3. Fundamental saturable-reactor circuit 60
4-4. Saturable reactor characteristics 62
4-5. Basic saturable reactor circuits 66
4-6. Three-legged saturable reactor 69
4-7. Magnetic leakage and core construction 72
4-8. Multiple control windings 76
4-9. Current and voltage relationships, forced magnetization 77
4-10. Natural magnetization 80
4-11. Load limitation 82
4-12. Parallel-connected a-c windings 82
4-13. Control response and time constant 84

5. Applications of saturable reactors   87

5-1. Introduction 87
5-2. Theatre-light control using saturable reactors 88
5-3. Electric furnace control 90
5-4. Battery charging control 92
5-5. Phase-shifting applications 93
5-6. Saturable-reactor circuits for d-c and oscillographic
     measurements 94
5-7. Polarity-sensitive saturable reactors 97
5-8. Resonant control circuits 100

6. The magnetic amplifier without feedback   102

6-1. Introduction 102
6-2. Basic magnetic-amplifier circuit 103
6-3. Load lines 105
6-4. Output (transfer) characteristics. 108
6-5. Multistage cascaded magnetic amplifiers 110
6-6. Compensation for quiescent load current effects . . . 111
6-7. Polarity-sensitive magnetic amplifiers 114
6-8. Balanced push-pull magnetic amplifiers 116
6-9. Magnetic amplifier power gains 119
6-10. Variable-gain push-pull magnetic amplifier 120

7. Applications of magnetic amplifiers without feedback   122

7-1. Introduction 122
7-2. Magnetic amplifier control of d-c motor speed . . . 122
7-3. Magnetic amplifier generator voltage regulation . . 125
7-4. Temperature control using magnetic amplifier . . . 126
7-5. Control of two-phase servo motor 129
7-6. Harmonic amplifier circuits 130
7-7. Magnetic amplifier discriminator 132

8. The magnetic amplifier with external feedback   135

8-1. Introduction 135
8-2. Gains of feedback amplifiers 137
8-3. Operation of the regenerative feedback amplifier . . 139
8-4. Elementary external feedback circuit. 140
8-5. Introduction of bias into external-feedback amplifier . 145
8-6. Push-pull external-feedback magnetic amplifier . . . 147
8-7. Four-reactor push-pull magnetic amplifier 150
8-8. Regenerative feedback snap action 151
8-9. A-c controlled feedback 152

9. The magnetic amplifier with internal feedback   155

9-1. Introduction 155
9-2. The basic internal-feedback magnetic amplifier . . . 156
9-3. Two-reactor internal-feedback amplifier 158
9-4. Two-reactor push-pull internal-feedback magnetic amplifier. 161
9-5. Biasing the internal-feedback amplifier 163
9-6. Compound feedback magnetic amplifier 163
9-7. Multistage internal-feedback amplifiers 165
9-8. Four-reactor push-pull magnetic amplifier 166
9-9. Three-phase magnetic amplifier 167
9-10. Push-pull flux detectors 169
9-11. Push-pull remote control positioning 170

10. Magnetic amplifier servomechanism applications   173

10-1. Introduction 173
10-2. Medium-power positioning servo system 175
10-3. Low-power instrument servo system 177

10-4. Synchro signal adapter servo system 179
10-5. Torque motor servo system 182
10-6. Magnetic servo amplifiers 182
10-7. High-speed magnetic servo amplifier 183

11. Educational magnetic amplifiers   188

11-1. Introduction 188
11-2. Basic educational magnetic amplifier. 188
11-3. Magnetic amplifier servo demonstrator 194

12. Miscellaneous circuits and applications   195

12-1. Introduction 195
12-2. A-c voltage regulation 195
12-3. Power supply voltage regulation. 198
12-4. D-c magnetic amplifiers 200
12-5. Magnetic amplifier dimmer 202
12-6. High-frequency saturable reactors 204
12-7. Regulating a d-c generator 206
12-8. Temperature control 207
12-9. Audio amplification 207
12-10. Magnetic reference standard 209

13. Properties and characteristics of magnetic amplifiers   210

13-1. Introduction 210
13-2. Advantages of magnetic amplifiers 211
13-3. Disadvantages of magnetic amplifiers 213
13-4. Rating specifications. 215
13-5. Commercial data 217

Appendices   225

A. Magnetic amplifier notation 226
B. Formulas 228
C. Answers to review questions 234

Index   235

CHAPTER

1

Introduction and History

~~~~~~

1-1. Introduction

The magnetic amplifier, like its familiar electron-tube or semi-conductor counterpart, is a device which reproduces an applied input signal at an increased amplitude, intensity, or power, without appreciably altering the signal's quality or form. Although all types of amplifiers have this common function, the methods by which they accomplish the action are vastly different. In the tube amplifier, small voltage variations between grid and cathode (input) control the number of electrons flowing from the cathode to the plate, and relatively large changes in plate voltage (output) are produced. A large degree of amplification, i.e., ratio between output voltage and input voltage, can be realized in the electron-tube device. In the semiconductor (transistor) amplifier, application of signal between the emitter and base (input) of the transistor produces large changes in resistivity between collector and base (output), thereby controlling the output current. Because the electrons are injected into the semi-conductor through a low input impedance and are collected through a high output impedance, amplification is produced in this unit.

In the magnetic amplifier, the flux variations in a core generated by a signal-derived current (input) flowing through a control winding on the core have a great effect on the impedance of a load winding (output) wound on the same core. In the simplest magnetic-amplifier device, the load winding, connected in series with the load and an a-c source, has maximum impedance when no control current is flowing. At this time, load power is at its minimum. When current flows in the control winding, the impedance of the load winding decreases, and greater output power is delivered to the load from the source. The wide range of fluctuation of load impedance caused by the signal applied to the control winding, and the ratio between output and input powers, produce the desired controllable high gain in the magnetic-amplifier device.

In its present state of development, and in view of its large number of applications, the magnetic amplifier has many advantages over other types of amplifying devices. It is a unit having extreme reliability, a long life, ruggedness, no warm-up time, high efficiency, a minimum of maintenance problems, and capable of high-temperature operation — and all these virtues in combination! Although the device does have certain disadvantages, as described in Chapter 13, it is felt that they will be eliminated or at least become less important as engineering know-how and production experience are gained. Packaged magnetic amplifiers are shown in Fig. 1-1.

Fig. 1-1. Packaged magnetic amplifiers. (*Courtesy, Magnetic Research Corporation.*)

1-2. Fundamentals of operation

Basically, the magnetic amplifier is derived from the saturable reactor (or saturable-core reactor), which consists of two windings placed on a core. The ferromagnetic core selected for this application has a highly rectangular magnetization (*B-H*) curve. One of the windings, the load winding, is connected in series with an a-c supply voltage and a load, while the other winding, the control winding, is

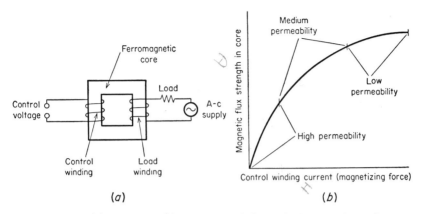

Fig. 1-2. (a) Basic saturable-reactor circuit from which magnetic amplifier is derived. (b) Relationship between control current and magnetic
flux in core, showing how core permeability varies.

fed by a control voltage, as shown in Fig. 1-2(a). The amplitude of
current flowing in the control winding determines the degree of core
magnetic saturation, which in turn controls the permeability of the
core (ratio between the magnetizing force and the magnetic flux
strength). This can be seen in Fig. 1-2(b). The inductance of the coil
and its inductive reactance are proportional to the core permeability.
Thus the impedance offered by the load winding to the a-c supply
voltage, and the voltage appearing across the load, are both affected
by the control current. For example, if the control winding drives the
core into magnetic saturation, the permeability is low, the load
winding impedance is low, the portion of a-c supply voltage appearing
across the load winding is low, and the voltage appearing across the
load itself is high. In effect, the fundamental reactor of Fig. 1-2(a)
acts as a switch between the load and the a-c power source, releasing
power to the load upon command from the control circuit. Amplification occurs because small changes in control current or power can
vary the state of the iron considerably, thereby controlling relatively
large powers.

This basic circuit operates without feedback. However, the introduction of regenerative feedback to the circuit can increase the usable
gain obtained from the magnetic amplifier by an exceedingly large
factor.* Bias, too, as in a tube amplifier, can be added to the circuit

---

* Magnetic amplifier feedback is subdivided into two major categories: external or
extrinsic, and internal or intrinsic. Large gains are obtainable in either case. Feedback is
discussed in Chapters 8 and 9.

to select a given point of operation, and thus increase the amplifier's utility.

1-3. Control characteristics of magnetic amplifiers

An amplifier is generally used in control applications to increase the power level of a control signal to that value required for operation of an associated load. It acts as the link between the data or control signal and the driven element of the system.

Prior to the development and utilization of the magnetic amplifier, and particularly in cases of large load power requirements, the thyratron and the amplidyne were used when power amplification was needed to obtain the large power outputs. The thyratron is a triode containing inert gas or mercury vapor under low pressure. The

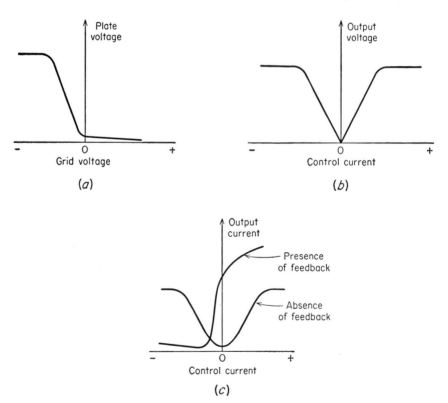

Fig. 1-3. (a) Control characteristic of a thyratron. (b) Control characteristic of an amplidyne. (c) Control characteristic of a magnetic amplifier.

introduction of the gas or vapor does not permit the tube's use as a grid-controlled amplifier, but rather makes it useful as a grid-controlled arc rectifier, having the control characteristic shown in Fig. 1-3(a). The thyratron may be controlled by either an a-c or d-c voltage input, but its output is necessarily d-c.

In its basic form, the amplidyne or rotary magnetic amplifier is a four-brush d-c generator having two brushes short-circuited together. The large armature current so produced provides a device which responds to changes of input in a control field and with a high degree of power gain. The amplidyne is controlled by a d-c current and supplies a large d-c power in the output. The input-output characteristic of the device is shown in Fig. 1-3(b).

The control characteristic of a magnetic amplifier differs radically between non-feedback and feedback states, as illustrated in Fig. 1-3(c). In both cases, however, the amplifier can be controlled by either alternating or direct current, and will provide either an alternating- or direct-current output.

Table 1-1 compares the thyratron, amplidyne, and magnetic amplifier with regard to their application in control circuitry. The thyratron has the advantage of a shorter response time and a higher power gain than the other devices. However, the magnetic amplifier is versatile in that it can be controlled by, and supply, either alternating or direct current, it uses a smaller quiescent power, and it occupies less space than the other amplifiers.

Table 1-1. Comparing Characteristics of Typical Control Devices

Device	Input control singal	Output power	Response time (msec)	Power gain	Quiescent power (watts)*	Size (cu ft)
Magnetic amplifier	a-c or d-c current	d-c or a-c	300	10^5	15	0.9
Thyratron	a-c or d-c voltage	d-c	1	10^6	40	1.6†
Amplidyne	d-c current	d-c	600	10^2	120	1.1

* In watts if controlled output power is 4 kw.
† Including associated transformer.

1-4. History of magnetic amplifiers

The magnetic amplifier is derived from the fundamental saturable reactor which was first described by C. F. Burgess and B. Frankenfeld in 1901. In their patent (claim filed in 1901 and issued in 1903), they discussed a means of regulating an electric current by the use of a variable-inductance saturable reactor.

Although some other patents were filed on the device in the interim, it appears that little practical importance was attached to its potentialities until E. F. W. Alexanderson, in 1916, described the gain properties of a saturable reactor in connection with a circuit for controlling (modulating) the output of a radio-frequency transmitter for radio telephone transmission. Because of the effectiveness of the circuit disclosed by Dr. Alexanderson, many transmitting stations, controlled by saturable reactors, were built and used during World War I.

Between the end of World War I and the start of World War II a large number of patents were filed covering aspects both of basic saturable reactors and more sophisticated magnetic amplifiers.* Despite the patent activity, little was accomplished in the United States by way of commercial application of the device although the literature of the time did contain references to the application of saturable reactors to lighting control systems, temperature control systems, voltage and frequency regulating devices, and phase shifters. This was not true in certain foreign countries, most notably Germany, where research and development had shown the magnetic amplifier to be an unusually reliable and practical unit. In general, the reactor in the magnetic amplifier may be subjected to the same treatment as a transformer without any appreciable change in its characteristics as long as the tolerable temperature and other environmental factors are observed for the materials used. Because reliability over a long service period is a requisite in most military control systems, much of the German World War II military equipment used magnetic amplifiers in a variety of ways, as in magnetic mines, autopilots in airplanes, and guided missiles.

With the data garnered from military applications, and with the development of suitable magnetic core material, particularly nickel-

---

* Generally the term *saturable reactor* is used in reference to a single reactor or group of reactors applied as a prime element in a circuit, whereas the term *magnetic amplifier* is applied to an over-all device consisting of saturable reactors and their associated components.

iron alloys having rectangular hysteresis loops, and compact, reliable dry-disc rectifiers, the magnetic amplifier came into its own in the post-war years. Progress was made in outlining the theory of operation of the device, which was complex by reason of the nonlinear characteristics of the magnetic core, and in developing techniques so that mass production methods could be adapted to the manufacture of magnetic amplifiers. Thus the development of equipment and methods for testing, matching, and grading cores, for encapsulating the units, for automatic toroidal winding, and for producing metallic rectifiers in large quantities has decreased the tolerances in the manufacture of the magnetic amplifier and thereby increased its utility. Moreover, applications of the device in the last decade have proved its practicality and advantages time and time again, and have assured that the future of the magnetic amplifier is bright indeed.

1-5. Significant patents in the magnetic amplifier art

Table 1-2* lists chronologically by filing date those patents filed with the United States Patent Office between 1901 and 1950 which are considered important in the historical development of the magnetic amplifier. It must be emphasized that the table does not indicate all patents dealing with the subject, but rather only those which are of significance.

---

* Presented by courtesy of *Transactions of the A.I.E.E.* and J. G. Miles.

Table 1-2. Significant Patents to Magnetic Amplifier Art

Patentee	United States Pat. No.	Filed	Issued	Reason selected
Burgess, C. F., and Frankenfield, B.	720,884	6–12–01	2–17–03	Early d-c saturable reactor. Control circuit decoupling means as follows: series impedance 3-legged and 4-legged cores, hollow annular cores, and magnetic "cross valve" core arrangements.
Crocker, F. B.	891,797	7–25–04	6–23–08	Early d-c saturable transformer. Control circuit decoupling means utilizing a 3-legged core.
Alexanderson, E. F. W.	1,206,643	12–07–12	11–28–16	First to mention gain properties. Early d-c saturable reactor with d-c bias means. Control circuit decoupling means employing two cores, also 4-legged cores.
Osnos, M.	1,227,302	7–08–15	5–22–17	Saturable reactors with 2-core and 3-legged core control circuit decoupling means.
Elmen, G. W.	1,289,418	11–23–15	1–31–18	Early Wheatstone bridge circuit employing signal-controlled reactor in one arm. Novel control means is by controlling the amount of agitating magnetomotive force to obtain variable hysteresis-effect reduction. Hollow annular core for circuit decoupling.
Alexanderson, E. F. W.	1,328,797	11–26–15	1–20–20	Early illustration of external feedback means. Control circuit decoupling means employing two cores, also 4-legged and 8-legged cores.
Alexanderson, E. F. W.	1,328,610	1–21–16	1–20–20	Early to claim off-resonant principle for increased gain. Also frequency discriminating means in a-c power supply and control circuits. Early illustration of cascaded magnetic amplifier stages.
Hartley, R. V. L.	1,462,038	12–30–16	7–17–23	A fundamental push-pull magnetic modulator.
Hartley, R. V. L.	1,287,982	2–16–17	12–17–18	D-c saturable transformer with ultra-carrier frequency magnetomotive force means for hysteresis effect reduction.
Stoekle, E. R.	1,376,978	11–24–17	5–03–21	Fundamental d-c saturable transformers with controlled-reluctance shunts; useful embodiments.
Alexanderson, E. F. W.	1,328,473	4–20–18	1–20–20	Means for utilizing a simple winding for the combined functions of saturation control, d-c bias, and as the reactance winding of a d-c saturable reactor.
Jonas, J.	1,434,346	10–04–20	10–31–22	Early full-wave d-c saturable reactor circuit with internal feedback. Control by d-c saturating winding.

Name	Patent No.			Description
Slepian, J.	1,645,302	4-21-21	10-11-27	A magnetic "self-modulator" (amplitude modulator) employing phase-controlled external feedback.
Heising, R. A.	1,654,932	6-29-22	1-03-28	A magnetic "self-modulator" (amplitude modulator) with external feedback.
Heegner, K.	1,656,195	10-23-25	1-17-28	Fundamental negative-resistance type magnetic self-modulator (amplitude modulator). Basic to the general class of magnetic amplifiers with negative resistance characteristics.
Lee, F. W.	Re. 19,129	10-30-26	4-03-34	Early means for obtaining zero output current from a magnetic amplifier in response to zero signal input. One embodiment utilizes "dummy" reactors. Early magnetic amplifier employing, though not claiming, Graetz-connected (full-wave bridge) copper-oxide rectifiers for demodulation.
Thomas, P.	1,734,239	9-23-27	11-05-29	A preferred winding configuration for 3-legged core d-c saturable transformers of Class B'.
Dowling, P. H.	1,739,579	6-20-28	12-17-29	Novel external feedback means comprising center-leg winding shorted by rectifier (for 3-legged cores only). Also novel d-c balancing means in d-c output circuit. Early permanent magnet d-c bias means. Combination circuits.
Dowling, P. H.	1,862,211	6-20-28	6-07-32	External feedback type and ferroresonant type magnetic "self-modulators" (amplitude modulators) in which the modulating frequency is determined by the R-L or L-C time constant of the control circuit.
Dowling, P. H.	1,878,764	6-20-28	9-20-32	Balanced magnetic amplifier comprising an output transformer with two opposing primary windings one of which is seriesed with the reactance winding of a controlling d-c saturable reactor. Zero stage output for zero control signal.
Peterson, E.	1,884,844	3-30-29	10-25-32	Fundamental negative-resistance type magnetic amplifier.
Dowling, P. H.	1,793,213	11-20-29	2-17-31	Magnetic amplifier comprising a Wheatstone-bridge-shaped core. Bridge balance is affected by controlling the magnetic reluctance of the bridge arms.
Dowling, P. H.	1,910,381	12-26-29	5-23-33	Novel magnetic amplifier type coincidence detector. D-c saturable reactors and transformers in novel combinations.
Sorensen, A. J.	1,824,577	2-07-30	9-22-31	Early Wheatstone bridge type magnetic amplifier. The four reactance arms of the bridge are the four reactance windings on two 3-legged reactors.
Dowling, P. H.	1,891,044	3-25-30	12-13-32	Early counter-acting a-c bias magnetomotive force at power supply frequency; means comprises shorting winding linking d-c control leg. Also novel balanced magnetic amplifier comprising d-c saturable reactor in combination with transformer. Novel core and winding configurations. Early external feedback type flip-flop.

Table 1-2. (cont.) Significant Patents to Magnetic Amplifier Art

Patentee	United States Pat. No.	Filed	Issued	Reason selected
Dowling, P. H.	1,835,209	6-23-30	12-08-31	D-c saturable reactors and transformers in novel combinations. Novel core and winding configurations are used.
Dowling, P. H.	1,862,212	6-23-30	6-07-32	Series ferroresonant circuit with flip-flop action. Also a novel d-c saturation controlled-balance transformer with opposing secondary windings.
Sorensen, A. J., and Dowling, P. H.	1,914,220	6-23-30	6-13-33	A group of significant and novel push-pull (balanced) magnetic amplifier circuits.
Peterson, E.	1,884,845	9-23-30	10-25-32	Variations on negative-resistance type magnetic amplifier.
FitzGerald, A. S.	1,914,201	10-02-30	6-13-33	Early phase-shift circuit employing a d-c saturable reactor as variable L.
Nagashev, B. V.	1,920,803	10-11-30	8-01-33	Wheatstone bridge type magnetic amplifier comprising a single 3-legged core with two bridge arm windings on each of the outside arms of the magnetic core. Bridge balance is affected by d-c magnetomotive force introduced in the center leg.
Sorensen, A. J.	1,862,204	12-06-30	6-07-32	Magnetic amplifier type combination coincidence detector and flip-flop.
Dowling, P. H.	1,842,392	12-12-30	1-26-32	D-c saturable reactors and transformers in novel combinations. Novel core and winding configurations are used.
Suits, C. G.	Re. 20,317	1-21-31	3-30-37	Nonlinear ferroresonant circuits to increase magnetic amplifier control sensitivity.
Zucker, M.	1,851,692	4-17-31	3-29-32	Wheatstone bridge type R-L phase-shift circuit employing a d-c saturable reactor as variable L. The R-L circuit is energized from a center-tapped impedance or transformer.
Logan, F. G.	1,997,179	5-07-31	4-09-35	Early internal feedback magnetic amplifier wherein the amount of positive internal feedback (net unidirectional flux) is controlled by means of a "flux normalizing" or a-c magnetomotive force-controlling impedance paralleled with the rectifier a-c input.
Schmidt, A.	1,921,703	11-13-31	8-08-33	Early multiple-saturation means for affecting the linearity and constancy of the reactance versus d-c control magnetomotive force characteristic of d-c saturable reactors.

Thomas, H. P.	2,016,977	12-01-31	10-08-35	Wheatstone bridge type magnetic amplifier employing peaked-waveform a-c power supply excitation to excite core to saturation. Nonlinear symmetrical resistive devices provide rectification for internal feedback and d-c output signal.
Logan, F. G.	2,068,188	8-03-32	1-19-37	Standard 3-legged core embodiment of internal feedback magnetic amplifier with control by saturating winding to supply d-c load.
Logan, F. G.	2,036,708	8-08-32	4-07-36	Novel d-c load current control scheme wherin a d-c saturable reactor is employed to variably load the secondary of a specially connected transformer, the primaries of which are seriesed with the a-c input of a full-wave rectifier.
Logan, F. G.	1,981,921	8-10-32	11-27-34	Early use of a-c bias at power supply frequency.
Power, J. R.	1,943,088	9-01-32	1-09-34	Wheatstone bridge type phase-shifter with variable L and parallel C off-resonant phase adjusting means
Boyajian, A.	2,040,684	12-23-32	5-12-36	Magnetic amplifier control circuit sensitivity-increasing means comprising series and parallel nonlinear ferroresonant circuits employing saturating reactors with controlled d-c bias. Where the circuit has leading current, it appears as a nonlinear capacitance, or saturating capacitance.
Logan, F. G.	1,986,112	5-11-33	1-01-35	Magnetic amplifier control-characteristic-exaggerating means comprising positive temperature coefficient resistor in shunt with d-c saturating (control) winding.
FitzGerald, A. S.	2,027,311	6-21-33	1-07-36	Schemes for improving the operation of cascaded magnetic amplifier stages. A reverse d-c bias is used in one embodiment to cancel the quiescent signal from the stage ahead. Also Wheatstone bridge and push-pull magnetic amplifiers.
FitzGerald, A. S.	2,021,099	7-27-33	11-12-35	A magnetic amplifier matrix method for randomly or successively energizing or de-energizing a plurality of loads one at a time from a single pair of d-c controlled inputs.
Antranikian, H.	2,047,609	8-25-33	7-14-36	Novel push-pull magnetic amplifier system employing Class B' d-c saturable transformers with pulsating unidirectional magnetomotive force applied via primary windings. Internal feedback by rectifiers in secondary circuits, novel means for compensating for rectifier leakage.
Suits, C. G.	1,968,576	9-23-33	7-31-34	Novel external feedback scheme comprising means for variably shunting the feedback circuit input impedance (here the secondary of a current transformer) to make negligible the temperature and aging characteristics of the dry-disc rectifier in the feedback circuit. Also novel embodiments: magnetic self-modulator and cascaded load sequencing circuit.

Table 1-2. (cont.) Significant Patents to Magnetic Amplifier Art

Patentee	United States Pat. No.	Filed	Issued	Reason selected
FitzGerald, A. S.	2,026,124	12-01-33	12-31-35	A modified Wheatstone bridge type magnetic amplifier capable of reciprocally and mediately indicating two balance conditions to two respective load circuits.
Burton, E. T.	2,164,383	1-29-34	7-04-39	Several "second harmonic" type magnetic amplifiers and binary flip-flops.
FitzGerald, A. S.	2,027,312	7-23-34	1-07-36	Single-sided d-c saturable reactor type magnetic flip-flop with two stable states.
Dellenbaugh, F. S., Jr.	2,175,379	12-31-34	10-10-39	Off-resonant type magnetic amplifier with novel means for inductively coupling the "parallel" C in order to make possible the use of a smaller C; the saturation control windings are utilized in the coupling scheme.
LaPierre, C. W.	2,053,154	3-27-35	9-01-36	Early "second harmonic type" magnetic amplifier. Employs a Class B' d-c saturable transformer with opposing secondaries. One embodiment is a magnetometer.
Edwards, M. A.	2,432,399	4-24-35	12-09-47	Wheatstone bridge type magnetic amplifier wherein the d-c saturating windings form a control bridge and the reactance windings are the reactance arms in the controlled reactance bridge.
Hanley, S. M.	2,144,289	8-26-35	1-17-39	Novel 3-legged reactor with unbalanced a-c flux path to purposefully create a-c flux in center leg. Control is by d-c saturating winding and by variably shunted winding on center leg. Two-core equivalent is shown.
Edwards, M. A., and Kane, G. A.	2,084,900	10-10-35	6-22-37	Wheatstone bridge type phase-shift circuit employing series L and C in one arm of the bridge.
Dawson, J. W.	2,140,349	10-23-35	12-13-38	Special magnetic amplifier to amplify changes in a-c power supply voltage. This is a simple external feedback magnetic amplifier without a separate control winding per se.
Logan, F. G.	2,118,440	3-30-36	5-24-38	Unique a-c bias means for control of special reactor which in turn controls d-c load. A-c control (bias) here is at magnetic amplifier power supply frequency. One-cycle control response is achieved.
Young, H. E.	2,154,020	4-09-36	4-11-39	Differentially balanced magnetic amplifier employing buck-boost d-c saturable transformer or d-c saturable reactor-controlled-transformer in a novel circuit arrangement.

Name	Patent No.	Filed	Issued	Description
Logan, F. G.	2,126,790	6-23-36	8-16-38	Basic d-c controlled internal feedback magnetic amplifier to control a-c load.
Boardman, E. M.	2,108,642	8-20-36	2-15-38	Two significant push-pull magnetic amplifiers with internal feedback. One of these magnetic amplifiers is of the "second harmonic" type.
Craig, P. H.	2,138,732	9-21-36	11-29-38	Magnetic amplifier control circuit sensitivity-increasing means employing series and parrallel L-C ferroresonant circuit combinations.
Burton, E. T.	2,147,688	12-02-36	2-21-39	Magnetic amplifiers and binary and ternary magnetic flip-flops and delay flop-flops. Some of the devices are of the "second harmonic" type.
Edwards, M.A.	2,169,093	1-02-37	8-08-39	Internal feedback magnetic amplifier to control a-c load. Novel features are d-c bias to compensate for no-load magnetizing flux and capacitor to neutralize load winding reactance. The possibility of a resonant-type magnetic amplifier flip-flop is noted.
Kalbskopf, W.	2,173,905	5-28-37	9-26-39	D-c saturable transformer with opposing secondary windings which are differentially balance-controlled such that the net output voltage is the difference voltage between the two seriesed secondaries. Balanced circuit possibilities exist.
FitzGerald, A. S.	2,168,402	1-11-38	8-08-39	Two single-sided flip-flops combined to form a self-oscillating flip-flop or multivibrator. The flip-flops are cross-connected by their saturation control windings.
O'Hagan, B. E.	2,215,823	6-10-38	9-24-40	D-c saturable transformer having two load energizing secondaries which are mediately and selectively excited in a reciprocal manner according to the amount of coupling of each with the primary as determined by the amount of d-c control magnetomotive force.
Whitely, A. L., and Ludbrook, L. C.	2,229,952	10-19-38	1-28-41	Two novel magnetic amplifiers — one is a nonpolarized magnetic amplifier with internal feedback to control a single d-c load. The other is a polarized magnetic amplifier without feedback to control one d-c load or to reciprocally control two d-c loads.
Hubbard, F. A.	2,218,711	12-30-38	10-22-40	Novel means for the controlled coupling of any one or more of a multiplicity of secondaries to the primary of a d-c saturable transformer. Novel permanent magnet d-c bias means.
Logan, F. G.	2,259,647	2-09-39	10-21-41	Unique a-c bias means for control of special reactor which in turn controls a-c load. A-c control (bias) here is at magnetic amplifier power supply frequency. One cycle control response is obtained.

13

Table 1-2. (cont.) Significant Patents to Magnetic Amplifier Art

Patentee	United States Pat. No.	Filed	Issued	Reason selected
Hines, C. M.	2,215,820	6-23-39	9-24-40	Novel embodiment of d-c saturable transformer having two load energizing secondaries the coupling of which to the primary is mediately, selectively and reciprocally controlled by the amount of d-c control magnetomotive force.
O'Hagan, B. E.	2,215,821	6-24-39	9-24-40	Novel embodiment of differentially balanced d-c saturable transformer having opposing secondary windings; the net output voltage is the difference voltage between the two seriesed secondaries. This is a balanced magnetic amplifier.
O'Hagan, B. E.	2,215,822	6-27-39	9-24-40	Novel d-c biasing means for Class B" d-c saturable transformers.
Geyger, W.	2,338,423	12-14-39	1-04-44	Cascaded Wheatstone bridge magnetic amplifier stages employing novel differentially connected d-c control windings to subsequent stages. Novel external feedback means for Wheatstone bridge magnetic amplifier. Novel Wheatstone bridge output means employing differential transformer.
Hornfeck, A. J.	2,310,955	12-30-39	2-16-43	Push-pull magnetic amplifier employing differentially cross-connected external feedback circuits to reciprocally affect one magnetic amplifier regeneratively and the other degeneratively depending on the polarity of the control signal.
McCreary, H. J.	2,324,634	1-31-40	6-20-43	D-c bias means for use in magnetic amplifiers. Permanent magnet bias means. A-c and d-c magnetic circuit separation and isolation means.
Stevens, S. A., and Walker, A. H. B.	2,222,048	2-21-40	11-19-40	Novel magnetic self-modulators and demodulators.
Krussmann, A.	2,399,872	10-24-40	5-07-46	Wheatstone bridge magnetic amplifier employing only one set of windings which are used for combined functions as d-c saturable control and as the reactance arms of the bridge.
Middel, H. D.	2,388,070	8-22-41	10-30-45	Novel d-c load controlling magnetic amplifier which does not employ rectifiers, but which employs, instead, symmetrical characteristic current distorting impedances which have no rectifying properties per se. High magnetic amplifier sensitivity is claimed.

Name	Patent No.	Filed	Issued	Description
Lamm, U.	2,403,891	9-23-42	7-09-46	Wheatstone bridge magnetic amplifier having external and internal feedback. Also Wheatstone bridge type magnetic flip-flop.
FitzGerald, A. S.	2,464,639	4-13-45	3-15-49	Novel d-c polarized push-pull magnetic amplifier. Novel features include impedance-coupled external feedback means to the control winding instead of to a special external feedback winding. Novel signal-limiters are used to avoid the deleterious effects of excessive control signals.
FitzGerald, A. S.	2,461,046	5-03-46	2-08-49	Novel Wheatstone bridge type magnetic amplifier.
Hedstrom, S. E.	2,509,864	6-19-46	5-30-50	Novel d-c polarized external feedback magnetic amplifier employing push-pull internal feedback magnetic amplifiers.
Forssell, H.	2,504,675	8-21-47	4-18-50	Novel d-c polarized balanced, single ended and push-pull magnetic amplifiers.
Tweedy, S. E.	2,475,575	10-29-47	7-05-49	Novel d-c polarized Wheatstone bridge type magnetic amplifier.
Graves, W. L. O.	2,516,563	4-19-48	7-25-50	Magnetic amplifier for the control of an inductive load. A rectifier limits the negative voltage across the inductive load to establish a mode of operation similar to that for a resistive load.
Lord, H. W.	2,509,738	4-29-48	5-30-50	Novel Wheatstone bridge magnetic amplifier with internal feedback.
Thompson, R. L.	2,519,513	9-09-48	8-22-50	Two-sided magnetic binary counter (flip-flop) with crossed external feedback.
Wood, M. L.	2,524,154	1-05-49	10-03-50	Two-sided magnetic flip-flop with crossed external feedback.

REVIEW QUESTIONS

1. Assume, in the circuit of Fig. 1-2(a), that the control voltage is 2 v initially, the a-c supply is 50 v, and that equal voltages appear across the load winding and the load resistance. If the control voltage is decreased, what happens to the voltages across the load winding and load resistance?

2. As the current in the control winding of a saturable reactor increases, the magnetic flux in the core increases [Fig. 1-2(b)]. What is the upper limit on the magnitude of useful control current?

3. Can a magnetic amplifier differentiate between negative and positive control currents? Explain your answer by referring to the characteristic curves of Fig. 1-3(c).

Elements of Magnetism

2-1. Introduction

Until the nineteenth century, magnetism was treated as a subject distinct from electromagnetism. From studies of permanent magnets, created by touching pieces of iron with natural magnets, magnetic properties were thought to be basically different in nature from the electromagnetic characteristics observed when an electric current was passed through a wire. However, the relationship between electricity and magnetism was first noted in 1821 when Oersted observed that a compass needle was deflected when placed in the vicinity of a current-carrying wire. Shortly afterward, Faraday and Henry demonstrated that current could be induced into a conductor which was moved through a magnetic field, thus further emphasizing the relationship between the two subjects. With the discovery of the electron in the latter part of the nineteenth century and with the advances made thereafter in understanding atomic and nuclear structures, it became evident that most observable magnetic effects were caused by the movement of electrons, whether this motion was progressive, as along the axis of a wire, or orbital, as in the planetary rotation around the nucleus of an atom. Thus, although magnetic and electromagnetic characteristics are sometimes described even today in a manner that tends to imply their independence, their common origin emphasizes that they should indeed be treated as one subject, or possibly as subsections under one subject. Indeed, the laws of magnetism which govern or interpret the actions of magnets are similar in many respects to the rules concerning the flow of electricity.

The importance of comprehending magnetic characteristics, principles, and terminology should not be underestimated since obviously the magnetic amplifier is predicated upon magnetic effects. On this basis, the material presented in this chapter is intended to serve as the foundation for all discussion of the magnetic amplifier to follow within this text.

2-2. History of magnetism

Magnetism and magnetic effects have been observed by man for many years dating from the original observation of the *natural magnet* or *lodestone* in the ancient district of Magnesia in Asia Minor. It was discovered there that certain stones (magnetite) taken from the earth had two unique characteristics: they could attract other similar stones or pieces of iron, and, when suspended from strings, elongated pieces of these stones would always point in a northerly direction. The first recorded use of magnetism appears to have been by the Chinese approximately 4600 years ago, indicating that the magnetic art is more ancient than most of the common sciences. In the year 2637 B.C., a Chinese emperor is alleged to have constructed a chariot upon which he mounted a figure carved from lodestone. Because the figure always faced south regardless of the direction in which this chariot moved, the emperor and his troops were enabled to roam the central plain of China during heavy fogs and under cover of darkness without losing their direction. Thus in its first application, the magnet was used in effect as a crude compass.

History also indicates that the lodestone was carried by the Greeks during their siege of Troy in about 1200 B.C., although the extent of its utility at that time is not now known. In due course of time, the knowledge of the magnet appears to have passed from the Chinese to the Arabs, and then to the Europeans. Its use as a compass was described by a Spanish Arab poet in A.D. 853, and writings indicate that it was known in Italy and Provence in about A.D. 1200. In the literature of the eleventh and twelfth centuries, many references are made to the use of the lodestone compass as a practical aid in marine navigations.

During the ensuing years, attempts were made to study the magnet and its effects, and works were published on the subject. A physicist, William Gilbert (1540-1603), expended a considerable effort in categorizing and recording magnetic effects. He was followed by others, such as Hans Christian Oersted (1771-1855), who noted that a compass needle was deflected in a similar fashion whether placed near a natural magnet or near a current-carrying wire; and Michael Faraday (1791-1867), who found that a current flowing in a wire could induce a current to flow in a nearby conductor; and Joseph Henry (1797-1878), who demonstrated that current could also be induced into a conductor by the motion of a magnet near it.

Although the history of magnetism is extensive in time and detail, the internal science itself is incomplete and, to this day, sketchy. One possible explanation for the lack of advance of the science lies perhaps in the emphasis placed on the permanent magnet (i.e., hard magnetic materials) throughout the years. With the advent of the electrical era in the latter part of the nineteenth century, the field of electromagnetic effects was first broached, and progress made in understanding basic magnetic principles and explaining basic magnetic phenomena.

2-3. Magnetic poles

When a magnet is examined, it is observed that the magnetic effects are not uniform over its surface, but rather appear to be concentrated in different regions of the body. In the case of a relatively long and thin magnet, these regions are near the ends, and are called the *poles* of the magnet. The imaginary straight line between the poles is called the *magnetic axis* of the magnet. If the magnet is suspended so that it can pivot freely, the magnet will rotate until it lines up in a general north-to-south direction. The pole which points north is referred to as the north pole of the magnet, or more properly, north-seeking pole. The other magnetic pole is the south or south-seeking pole. (See Art. 2-6.)

The poles of a magnet are regions, not mathematical points, and are not precisely at the ends of the magnet. Despite this, and for ordinary magnetic computations, it can be assumed with little error that the poles of a long bar magnet (one in which the magnet length is 50 or more times greater than the width) are at the ends, and that the length of the magnet is the separation between the poles.

Theoretically, it is impossible to isolate a single magnetic pole. However, the forces acting between north and south poles of a magnet decrease rapidly as the distance between the poles increases. For practical purposes, then, single isolated poles may be considered to be obtained at the ends of a long, thin bar magnet.

2-4. Attraction and repulsion of magnets; Coulomb's law

If two bar magnets are brought together, it is noted that the north pole of one repels the north pole of the other and, in similar fashion, the south poles repel each other. However, when the north pole of one magnet is placed near the south pole of the other, magnetic attraction occurs. Basically, then, like magnetic poles repel while unlike poles attract. (This magnetic law is similar to that which governs charged bodies.)

In 1785, the French scientist Coulomb studied the forces involved in the attraction and repulsion of magnetic poles. As a result, he concluded that the force of attraction or repulsion between poles of fixed strength is proportional to the product of the pole strengths (the greater the pole strengths, the larger the force), but inversely proportional to the square of the distance separating the poles (the greater the distance of separation, the smaller the force). Coulomb also observed that the magnitude of the force is affected by the medium in which the magnetic poles are located. This property of the medium is called its permeability; it will be described in greater detail in Art. 3-3. Because the value of permeability of vacuum is 1, and that of air is very close to 1, the magnetic force of attraction or repulsion in vacuum or air is determined only by the strength of the poles and the distances separating them.

In summary, then, the force existing between poles, as given by Coulomb's law, is

$$F = \frac{m_1 m_2}{\mu d^2} \qquad (2\text{-}1)$$

where F = the force of attraction or repulsion
m_1 and m_2 = strength of the magnetic poles
μ = permeability of the medium in which the poles are located
d = distance between poles.

2-5. The magnetic field

The region surrounding a magnet, in which appreciable magnetic forces exist and are capable of being detected, is referred to as the *magnetic field*. Theoretically the field produced by a magnet extends indefinitely in all directions; practically, however, the field strength diminishes rapidly as the distance from the poles of the magnet is increased. The magnetic field strength at any given point is the force, due to the magnetic field (as produced by a bar magnet, for example), acting upon an isolated (unit) magnetic north pole placed at the point. The isolated north pole simultaneously encounters a repelling force caused by the north pole of the bar magnet and an attracting force caused by its south pole. The resultant force, then, is considered to be the magnetic field strength at the given point. Furthermore, since the isolated magnetic north pole would tend to move toward the south pole of the bar magnet, the general direction of the magnetic field is taken from north pole to south pole.

Since the magnetic field is invisible and intangible, and as such is difficult to visualize and express, a method has been adopted in which the field is represented by means of *lines of magnetic force* or *lines of magnetic induction*. These imaginary lines of force are usually drawn such that their direction at any point is that of the magnetic field to which they correspond, and their number per unit area represents the magnetic field strength. Further, these lines are considered to follow definite rules, namely:

   a. The magnetic lines of force are continuous, and close in on themselves to form closed loops. They leave a magnet at its north pole, travel externally in definite paths to the south pole, and then return from south to north pole within the iron.
   b. The lines of force never cross each other.
   c. The lines of force are assumed to be capable of passing through any material, but they tend to choose the path of least resistance.

The distribution of the lines of force surrounding a bar magnet may be examined by sprinkling iron filings on a sheet of paper placed over the magnet. The filings become magnetized by induction, and when the paper is tapped lightly, they arrange themselves in regular lines between the poles. The lines of force are, of course, close to each other near the poles of the magnet, since magnetic strength is greatest at these points.

In the electromagnetic system of units, a *maxwell* is the name given to each single line of force. A *gauss* is the magnetic field strength which occurs when one maxwell occupies one square centimeter of area. The total number of lines of force in any given area or surface is referred to collectively as the magnetic flux or Φ. The magnetic flux may be defined as

$$\Phi = BA \tag{2-2}$$

where Φ = magnetic flux, in maxwells
     B = lines of magnetic force, in gausses
     A = area through which the flux passes, in square centimeters.

2-6. The earth's magnetic field

It was stated in preceding articles that (1) a bar magnet freely suspended will always line up in a general north-to-south direction, and (2) like poles repel, unlike poles attract. Based upon these facts, it has been concluded that the earth acts as a magnet, with poles situated near the geographical poles, and that a magnetic field surrounds the earth. In 1840, Gauss showed that the distribution of the field is the same as would be produced by a huge bar magnet placed near the center of the earth with its magnetic axis inclined about 20 degrees from the axis of rotation of the earth. The earth's magnetic poles exert a force on the freely suspended magnet (which is, in effect, a compass) such that the south pole of the magnet is attracted to the earth's north pole. Thus the terminology "north-seeking pole" and "south-seeking pole" is clarified when the action of a compass is considered; the end of the compass magnet which points toward the earth's north magnetic pole is actually the south pole of the magnet, or, more correctly, its north-seeking end.

Although 90 per cent of the magnetic field existing at the surface of the earth may be explained by assuming uniform magnetization of the material within the earth, the complete theory of the earth's field has not yet been verified. One such theory indicates that a space charge exists in the upper atmosphere causing an electric current to flow in an east-to-west direction about the earth. The current flow, it is assumed, produces the remaining 10 per cent of the earth's field.

2-7. Classification of magnetic materials

It was common practice at one time to classify materials into two main magnetic groups for the purposes of discussion. The materials that were easily magnetized were considered as magnetic; all others were classified as nonmagnetic. Upon further investigation, it was soon learned that almost all materials are affected to some degree when placed in a strong magnetic field. On the basis of this discovery, it is now usual to place a material into one of three groups, as determined by the manner and extent that the material is affected by an external magnetizing force.

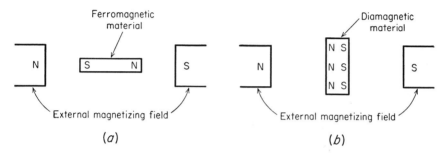

Fig. 2-1. (a) Action of a ferromagnetic material in an external magnetizing field. (b) Action of a diamagnetic material in an external magnetizing field.

Ferromagnetic materials are those which, when placed in an external magnetizing field, become strongly magnetized in the direction of the field. This grouping is shown in Fig. 2-1(a), where it is noted that the polarities induced in a ferromagnetic material are opposite those of the external field, and that the longer axis of the material lines up with the field. Materials such as iron, steel, nickel, cobalt, magnetite, and alloys such as Permalloy and Alnico, all of which are ferromagnetic, have a high value of permeability; that is, they permit the easy passage of magnetic lines of force. Their permeability is not constant; it depends, among other things, on the strength of the external magnetizing field. Cores of magnetic amplifiers are constructed of ferromagnetic materials.

Paramagnetic materials are those which become only weakly magnetized in the direction of the external magnetizing field. The distinction between ferromagnetism and paramagnetism lies in the degree, not in the direction, of magnetization. Paramagnetic materials are aluminum, platinum, manganese, air, and chromium, all of which have a permeability greater than one.

Diamagnetic materials are those which become weakly magnetized in the presence of an external magnetizing field, but in a direction opposite to that of the field. This may be observed in Fig. 2-1(b), where it may be seen that the polarities induced into the material are the same as those of the external field, causing the material to line up with its longer axis perpendicular to the direction of the field. Materials such as bismuth, antimony, copper, phosphorus, gold, and silver, all of which have a permeability of less than unity, belong in this classification.

The most important magnetic materials used in industry today are iron and its alloys, the ferromagnetic group. These materials have a crystalline structure, and are characterized by large values of permeability.

2-8. Introduction to magnetic theory

Many theories have been brought forth which purport to explain magnetism. One of the theories developed prior to the advent of modern physics was expounded by Weber and Ewing in what is known as the *molecular theory of magnetism.* According to this theory, all magnetic materials consist of individual molecular magnets. These

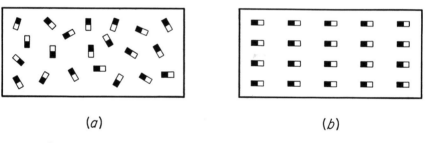

(a)   (b)

Fig. 2-2. Molecular theory of magnetism (I): (a) unmagnetized material; (b) magnetized material.

minute magnets are capable of movement within the material. When a magnetic material is in its unmagnetized state, the individual magnetic particles are arranged at random, and effectively neutralize each other so far as external effects are concerned. An example of this is shown in Fig. 2-2(a), where the tiny magnetic particles are arranged in a disorganized manner. (The north poles are represented by the darkened ends of the magnetic particles.) When a material is magnetized, the individual particles are aligned or oriented in a definite direction, Fig. 2-2(b). External magnetic effects are readily detected in this case. The degree of magnetization of a material depends, according to this theory, on the degree of alignment of the particles. Thus the particles in a weak magnet are more or less aligned in a definite direction, although many of the individual particles are out of alignment. On the other hand, all of the particles in a strong magnet are in definite and specific alignment. Obviously, when all of the molecular magnets are located so that their axes are parallel to each other, the limit of magnetization has been reached, and the material may be thought to be magnetically saturated.

The action of an external magnetization field on the particles in a magnetic material may be understood by reference to Fig. 2-3. In (a), the particles in the material are shown as they would appear if free to turn in the absence of any field. In (b), the particles are being subjected to a weak magnetic field; they turn slightly in the direction of the field. As the field intensity is increased (c), the particles more

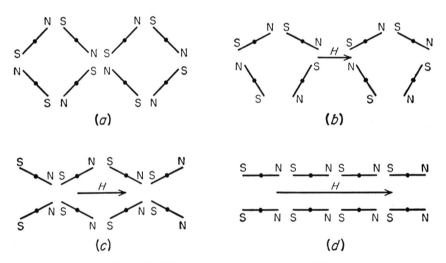

Fig. 2-3. Molecular theory of magnetism (II).

nearly line up in the direction of H, until finally in (d), they are fully aligned. At this time, there is a preponderance of north poles pointing toward one direction, and south poles pointing in the opposite direction. At the center of the magnetic material, the effect of each individual pole is neutralized by that of the neighboring pole of opposite polarity.

The alignment of particles may occur through the workings of nature, as in the case of a lodestone, or may be produced by the presence of an external magnetizing force (Fig. 2-3), such as that due

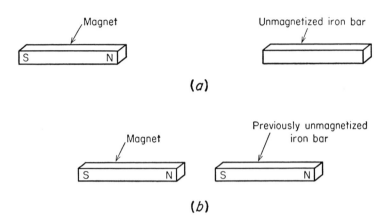

Fig. 2-4. Magnetic induction: (a) when magnet and unmagnetized iron are apart; (b) when magnet is placed near unmagnetized bar, and bar becomes magnetized by induction.

to current passing through a coil, or by *magnetic induction.* This last case refers to the situation which arises when one pole of a permanent magnet is brought near the end of an unmagnetized iron bar. If the pole which approaches the unmagnetized bar is the north pole, the bar becomes magnetized in such direction that the end of the bar nearest to the north pole of the magnet becomes the south pole of the bar, while the far end of the bar becomes the north pole. This is shown in Fig. 2-4(a) and (b). The magnetic effects of the artificially produced magnet are identical to those of the natural magnet. When the inducing magnet is moved away, the magnetic particles in the bar tend to return to their original orientation, and the bar loses its magnetic qualities. The extent to which the bar returns to its original unmagnetized state depends upon its previous orientation, and upon the material.

Magnetic induction can be used to explain the method by which a magnet attracts an unmagnetized piece of iron. When the magnet is placed near the iron, the iron becomes magnetized through induction, and the end of the iron closest to the magnetic pole assumes an opposing polarity. As a result, a force of attraction occurs, and the magnet tends to cling to the iron. It should also be noted in passing that a piece of iron which is magnetized by induction can induce magnetism into another piece of iron placed near it. This process can be repeated through several pieces of iron, although the strength of the induced poles progressively decreases.

Weber and Ewing in propounding the molecular theory of magnetism predicated their theory on the assumption that the molecular particles were actually tiny permanent magnets. Ampere, in examining the theory, made the further assumption that the molecular particles behaved as magnets because of currents circulating continuously within the atoms. The modern theory of magnetism as conceived by the physicist is based on the concept of *spinning electrons* and a *critical atomic distance*.

The atom, as we presently understand it, consists of a nucleus with a positive charge, around which electrons move in orbital paths, as seen in Fig. 2-5 for the iron atom. According to present theory, individual planetary electrons are not only moving around the nucleus, but at the same time are spinning about an axis through the center of each electron. Some of the electrons are considered to be spinning in one direction (as indicated by a + sign in Fig. 2-5); others are spinning in the opposite direction (− sign, Fig. 2-5). If in any given atom the number of electrons spinning in one direction is the same as the number spinning in the opposite direction, the material exhibits little or no ferromagnetic qualities. Thus if a nonmagnetized iron atom is examined, it will have 13 plus electron spins and 13 minus

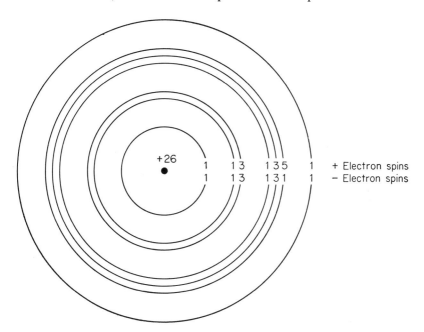

Fig. 2-5. Atomic structure and electron spins in the iron atom.

electron spins. If, however, an imbalance exists in the spinning electrons such as is produced when a ferromagnetic material is subjected to a magnetizing force, ferromagnetism results. Thus in the case of the iron atom illustrated in Fig. 2-5, the total number of plus spins is 15 and the total number of minus spins is 11, with the imbalance being produced in the orbital path once removed from the outermost or valence orbit. This atom will exhibit magnetic qualities.

The imbalance of spinning electrons in any single atom cannot produce detectable ferromagnetism if the adjacent atoms have imbalances which cancel it. It is essential that adjacent atoms complement, rather than detract, from the magnetic effects produced by the electron spins. At this point, modern magnetic theory introduces the *critical atomic distance*. When atoms are separated by large distances, their spins cannot complement each other, and ferromagnetism does not exist to any great degree. When atoms are close, it is assumed that certain atomic exchange forces become operative, causing the electron spins to complement each other, such that ferromagnetic effects arise. The closer the atoms, the greater are the magnetic characteristics exhibited by the material. However, at a specified critical atomic distance, all electron spins tend to cancel each other, and magnetic effects are no longer detectable.* Examination of magnetic materials has disclosed that the critical atomic distance is a function of the distance between atoms, as described above, and of the diameter of the unbalanced electron orbits.

The exchange forces between atoms tend to cause the electron spins of adjacent atoms to align with each other. It is found, however, that the alignment does not extend over a complete ferromagnetic material, but rather is limited to small sections of the material. Thus the outer material is, in effect, composed of thousands or millions of these small sections, called *domains*. In each domain the electron spins are parallel, and each domain is consequently magnetized to saturation in a given direction. A ferromagnetic material is considered as unmagnetized when the aggregation of all the random directions of magnetization of the domains is zero.

If a small external magnetizing force is applied to an unmagnetized material, those domains whose orientation is close to that of the direction of the field expand slightly, at the expense of the size of those

---

* A detailed explanation of this theory involves a discussion of atomic exchange forces as described in quantum mechanics, which is beyond the scope of the book.

domains which are of different orientation. As the field is increased further, a different mode of magnetization is produced. Now other domains shift into the direction of magnetization of the field by a shift of the axial spins of the electrons. Each shift is accompanied by an expansion in volume of the new domain.* If the external magnetizing force is plotted against the resultant flux density in the material, the plotted curve appears to be perfectly smooth; it is, in actuality, the result of a series of discrete jumps in the magnetic flux density (called the Barkhausen effect). Because of these jumps, the action is not reversible, thus explaining the hysteresis effect. (See Arts. 3-7 and 3-8.) As the magnetizing force continues to increase, the realignment of the domains continues rapidly until it is quite complete. As the external magnetizing force is increased further, all domains not in complete alignment are rotated into position. At saturation, all domain electron spins are parallel to the applied field.

REVIEW QUESTIONS

1. A magnetic north pole with a strength of 40 unit poles is placed 10 cm from a magnetic south pole having a strength of 50 unit poles. (a) If the poles are in a medium which has a permeability of 2, what is the force acting between the poles? Assume that F is in dynes and d is in centimeters in Eq. (2-1). (b) Is the resultant force one of attraction or repulsion? (c) If the distance is decreased to 2 cm, what happens to the force?

2. Two magnetic north poles of 160 and 360 poles are placed in vacuum. If a force of 1000 dynes acts between the poles, what is the distance in centimeters between the poles?

3. What are the rules which govern the representation of the lines of magnetic induction?

4. A magnetic pole has a flux (Φ) of 200,000 maxwells, acting uniformly over an area which measures 2 cm wide by 5 cm long. How many magnetic lines of force, in gausses, occupy each square centimeter of area?

5. Using Fig. 2-4(b), sketch the lines of magnetic force to show how magnetic induction causes the unmagnetized iron bar to assume the illustrated magnetic polarity.

---

* This is the phenomenon of magnetostriction, in which the dimensions of a magnetic material change under the influence of an external field.

Electromagnetism and
Electromagnetic Induction

‑‑

3-1. Magnetic effects of current

About 1820, Oersted discovered that a magnetic field existed around a conductor through which electrons were flowing. This effect is easily verified by placing a compass near the conductor. In the absence of current flow, the compass acts normally: the compass needle lines up in a north-to-south direction. When current flows through the conductor, the needle is deflected in a manner similar to the way the needle moves when placed near a bar magnet. The immediate assumption can be made that the field surrounding a bar magnet has the same characteristics as the field surrounding a current-carrying conductor.

The magnetic field around a conductor appears in the form of concentric lines of magnetic force, as shown in Fig. 3-1. The direction of the lines is determined by the direction of the electron flow in the conductor: when the electric flow is reversed, the direction of the lines is reversed. The lines of force are concentrated in the area near the conductor, and the magnetic effects are strong here. The field

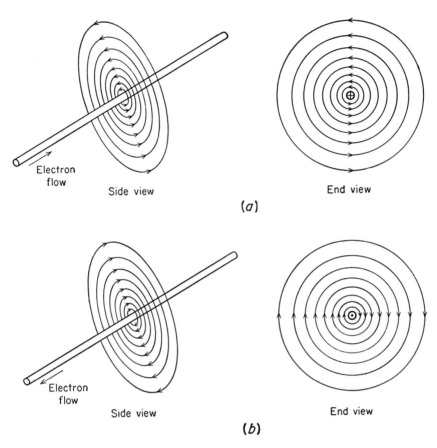

Fig. 3-1. Magnetic field produced by current flow in a conductor: (a) electron flow into plane of paper; (b) electron flow out of plane of paper.

strength decreases rapidly as the distance from the conductor increases.

The direction of the lines of flux around a straight conductor may be determined by using the conductor "left-hand rule" as follows: When the conductor is grasped with the left hand so that the thumb points in the direction of the electron flow, the fingers point in the direction of the magnetic lines of force.

The converse of this rule also holds true. Thus, to determine the electron flow in a conductor when the direction of the lines of force is known, grasp the conductor with the left hand so that the fingers point in the direction of the lines of force; the thumb points in the direction of the electron flow.

3-2. Magnetic field about a solenoid

If a conductor is wound on a hollow form as shown in Fig. 3-2(a), a solenoid is produced. When an electron flow passes through the solenoid, as in Fig. 3-2(b), a magnetic field appears around each loop of wire in the solenoid. This may be seen by examining Fig. 3-3.

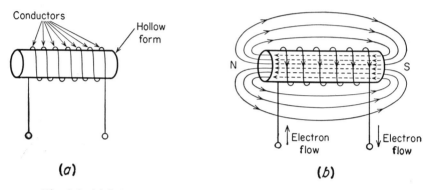

(a)   (b)

Fig. 3-2. (a) Solenoid wound on a hollow form. (b) Magnetic field and polarity produced by electrons flowing in solenoid.

In (a), the conductors under consideration are separated by a relatively large distance. The lines of force existing between the two conductors are in opposite directions, thereby tending to cancel. In (b), the conductors are in close proximity, as they are in a solenoid, so that no lines of force appear between the conductors, but rather tend to encircle them. For a solenoid, then, the primary magnetic effects appear at its ends. Thus, the magnetic field surrounding the solenoid corresponds in many respects to the field of a bar magnet, and the solenoid shows evidence of poles at its ends [Fig. 3-2(b)]. The polarity of a solenoid may be deduced from the "solenoid left-hand rule":

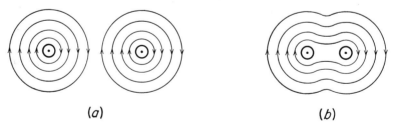

(a)   (b)

Fig. 3-3. Magnetic fields produced around adjacent conductors: (a) distance between conductors relatively large; (b) distance between conductors relatively small.

When the solenoid is grasped with the left hand so that the fingers point in the direction of the electron flow, the thumb points in the direction of the north pole.

Although not indicated in Fig. 3-2(b), some lines of force do emerge from the sides of the solenoids, in addition to the main field from the ends. Because of this, the poles of a solenoid are less distinct areas than those of a bar magnet.

When an iron core is placed within the hollow form of the solenoid, the magnetic field strength produced by a current flow of given magnitude increases radically. This results because the lines of force passing through the core cause it to become magnetized by induction. The total magnetic field strength is the resultant of the solenoid field and the field produced by the iron. The solenoid with iron core is referred to as an *electromagnet*. The field distribution of the electro-magnet shows fewer lines issuing from its surface than from the pure solenoid. The lines of force, it will be recalled, tend to take the path of least resistance, which is through the iron; i.e., iron has a high value of permeability. Thus, the poles of the electromagnet are more definitely located at the ends than in the case of the solenoid.

3-3. The magnetic circuit and magnetic terminology

Magnetomotive Force. In an electric circuit, the current that flows is assumed to be caused by an electromotive force. By analogy, the flux produced in a magnetic circuit may be considered as caused by a *magnetomotive force* (abbreviated mmf). This force may issue from a magnetized body or may be caused by the current flowing in a wire, coil, or electromagnet.

In the cgs electromagnetic (emu) system of units, magnetomotive force is described in terms of the *gilbert*, and is defined by the equation

$$F = 0.4\pi NI \text{ gilbert} \tag{3-1}$$

where I is the current in amperes flowing in the conductor or con-ductors, and N is the number of turns of conductor through which the current is passing. The product NI is frequently referred to as the ampere turns of the magnetic circuit.

Magnetic Flux. The analogy between the electric circuit and the magnetic circuit is also helpful in understanding the term *magnetic flux*, which refers to the total number of lines of force in a given area.

It will be recalled that Ohm's law for an electric circuit states that

$$\text{current} = \frac{\text{electromotive force (emf)}}{\text{resistance}}$$

or
$$I = \frac{E}{R}$$

Similarly, in a magnetic circuit

$$\text{flux} = \frac{\text{magnetomotive force (mmf)}}{\text{reluctance}}$$

or
$$\Phi = \frac{F}{\Re} \tag{3-2}$$

From Eq. (3-2), it can be seen that the flux Φ in a magnetic circuit is dependent directly upon the magnetomotive force of the circuit and inversely upon its reluctance, the latter referring, in effect, to the opposition the circuit offers to flux. In the emu system of units, the unit of flux is the *maxwell*.

The characteristics of the lines of force which make up the magnetic flux were summarized in Art. 2-5.

Magnetizing Force or Magnetic Intensity. The magnetomotive force of a magnetic circuit may be applied over a large or small area (magnetic circuit length). In the latter case, the magnetic intensity per unit space of area will be greater. This intensity, or magnetizing force H, is expressed in *oersteds,* and at any point in a magnetic circuit is measured by the number of gilberts per centimeter at that point. Thus, the magnetizing force for a uniform magnetic field (one in which each square centimeter contains the same number of maxwells) is

$$H = \frac{F}{l} \text{ oersted} \tag{3-3}$$

where F is the magnetomotive force in gilberts and l is the length of the magnetic circuit in centimeters. With reference to Eq. (3-1), it can be seen that

$$H = \frac{0.4\pi NI}{l} \text{ oersted} \tag{3-3a}$$

Flux Density. The flux density B refers to the unit density of magnetic flux over a surface. It is measured in terms of the *gauss,* and is defined (for a uniform magnetic field) as

$$B = \frac{\Phi}{A} \text{ gauss} \qquad (3\text{-}4)$$

where Φ is the magnetic flux in maxwells for an area A, and A is the area in square centimeters over which the flux is distributed. One gauss then expresses a flux density of one maxwell per square centimeter. Since flux densities are usually in the order of thousands of maxwells per square centimeter, a more practical unit is the kilogauss.

Permeability. The permeability μ is a measure of the ease with which magnetic flux passes through a material. Its value for vacuum is chosen as unity, and the permeabilities of other substances are compared with that of empty space. Good magnetic materials — i.e., materials through which lines of force pass readily — are found to have a high value of permeability, while nonmagnetic materials have a value close to that of vacuum, or one.

In the cgs electromagnetic system of units, the ratio between the magnetizing force H and the flux density B defines the permeability, such that

$$\mu = \frac{B}{H} \qquad (3\text{-}5)$$

Thus, in vacuum (and this is very nearly correct for air and other magnetic materials as well), one oersted of magnetizing force will produce one gauss of flux density. The ratio between the magnetizing force and the flux density is not constant, so that the permeability of magnetic materials is variable. This characteristic is described in Art. 3-6.

Reluctance and Permeance. The permeance (P) of a magnetic circuit refers to its ability to pass magnetic flux. As such, the terms permeance and reluctance, where reluctance may be defined as the opposition offered by a material to the passage of flux, are reciprocals of each other; namely

$$\mathcal{R} = \frac{1}{P}$$

Thus, a circuit of unit permeance would have a reluctance of unit, but for all other cases, the greater the permeance, the smaller is the reluctance, and vice versa. The reluctance depends upon the length of the core path, the core cross-sectional area, and the core permeability.   Neither reluctance nor permeance has a universally accepted name for its unit.

Although it is true that the term reluctance as used in the magnetic circuit corresponds to resistance in the electric circuit, it has the additional characteristic that its value for magnetic materials is not a constant, but rather varies as the flux density is changed. On the other hand, the reluctance of nonmagnetic materials is constant.

3-4. Magnetic units

In the definitions given in the preceding articles, the cgs electromagnetic units were employed, since they are usually used to define magnetic qualities. However, the engineer or technician may encounter the mks (or practical) units or the mixed English units (mEu) in the literature. Table 3-1 illustrates the relationships between the units. Equality signs are implied across any one horizontal row in the table; i.e., 1 maxwell equals 10^{-8} weber.

Table 3-1. Relations between Magnetic Qualities in the Different Systems of Units

Entity	Symbol	Cgs electro-magnetic unit	Mks practical unit	Mixed English unit	Electro-static unit
Flux	Φ	1 maxwell (1 line of force)	10^{-8} weber	1 line	$\frac{1}{3} \times 10^{-10}$
Flux density	B	1 gauss (1 line per sq cm)	10^{-4} weber/meter^2	0.155 line/sq in.	$\frac{1}{3} \times 10^{-10}$
Magnetizing force	H	1 oersted (1 gilbert per cm)	0.25×10^3 ampere turn/meter	0.494 ampere turn/in.	3×10^{10}
Magneto-motive force	F	1 gilbert	0.7958 ampere turn	1.26 ampere turn	3×10^{10}
Permeability	μ	1 gauss/oersted	$4\pi \times 10^{-7}$ henry/meter	—	$\frac{1}{9} \times 10^{20}$ (sec/cm)^2
Reluctance	$\Re$	1	7.958×10^7 ampere turn/weber	—	9×10^{20}

3-5. The magnetic and electric circuits

Although it is helpful to compare the magnetic circuit to the electric on the basis of similarities between them, it must be emphasized that the two circuits are essentially different. For example, the electric circuit implies that an act of flowing is occurring — i.e., electrons are flowing through the circuit. No such action occurs in the magnetic circuit. The presence of magnetic flux indicates merely that a state of magnetic strain has been produced in the material of the circuit.

Another difference is that a continuous source of power is required to maintain a current in an electric circuit, where power is dissipated continually, while magnetic flux, once established, requires no power dissipation at all, as witness the flux of a permanent magnet. The power expended in the winding of an electromagnet takes place not in the magnetic circuit but rather in the electric, and is the result of the resistance of the conductor.* The analogy between the circuits also breaks down when one considers that it is quite possible to confine an electric current almost entirely to its desired path, while it is almost impossible (with but one main exception) to confine flux wholly to a definite and distinct path. This derives from the fact that a good conductor in an electric circuit may have a conductivity of approximately 10^{20} times that of a good insulator, whereas the permeability of a good magnetic material may be only 10^3 times that of a nonmagnetic material. In effect, then, no material exists which might be considered as a magnetic insulator, and flux cannot be channeled with any great degree of definiteness. The sole exception to this is the ring solenoid; in this case, no magnetic poles are produced and the magnetic flux lies entirely within the solenoid.

Another notable difference between the two circuits is that the resistance of an electric circuit is not dependent upon the current flowing in the circuit, while the reluctance of a magnetic circuit is affected by the strength of the magnetic flux.

3-6. The magnetization, or *B-H* curve

The permeability of a ferromagnetic material is not constant, but rather variable, and depends to a great degree upon the magnitude of the applied magnetizing force H. Furthermore, the curve relating flux density B and magnetizing force H cannot be described mathematically with any degree of accuracy; however, it can be plotted accurately in the laboratory.

---

*The power losses in the magnetic core of a coil or electromagnet do not result from the characteristics of an alternating magnetic flux, but rather from the properties of the core.

To understand the derivation of the magnetization curve, consider a piece of completely demagnetized ferromagnetic material placed within a magnetizing coil. If the current flowing through the coil is increased gradually from zero to a maximum value, so that the magnetic intensity of the coil increases, the flux density in the specimen material will also increase. Further, if the values of the external magnetizing force are at all points plotted against the measured values of the magnetic flux density, the result is a *B-H* curve, also called a *magnetization* or *saturation* curve.

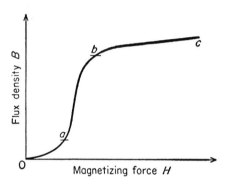

Fig. 3-4. A typical magnetization (*B-H*) curve of a ferromagnetic material.

A typical *B-H* curve is shown in Fig. 3-4. An examination of it indicates that the process of magnetization in a ferromagnetic material can be divided roughly into three major stages. In the first section, as defined by the 0*a* portion of the curve, increases in the magnetizing force *H* produce slow increases in the flux density *B*. The initial slope of the curve, indicating permeability, is small. In addition, *B* is almost directly proportional to *H*. Permeabilities of up to 100 are found in this region. In the second stage, *ab* in Fig. 3-4, further increases in *H* produce an abrupt and rapid increase in the value of *B*. During this interval, the curve rises sharply, and its slope is steep and fairly constant. The permeability in this region may range between 4000 and 5000. In the section *bc*, the slope of the curve decreases rapidly as a state of magnetic saturation is approached. During this interval, increases in the applied magnetizing force lead to essentially linear increases in the magnetic flux, although at a much decreased rate. After saturation, any additional increase in *H* will produce a small increase in *B*. Thus the top of the *B-H* curve is not strictly horizontal, but the ratio *B/H* is so small that its effect is negligible.

The magnetic flux density of Fig. 3-4 is in actuality the sum of two components. The first is the flux density which is present in any material, ferromagnetic or not, when it is subjected to an external magnetizing force. The value of this component is dependent upon the magnitude of the applied *H*, and increases linearly at a low rate as

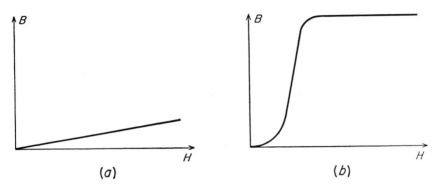

Fig. 3-5. (a) Flux density component independent of ferromagnetic properties. (b) Flux density resulting from ferromagnetic properties.

H increases. This is shown in Fig. 3-5(a). Its value is the product of the permeability of vacuum and the magnetizing force, or $\mu_v H$. The second component is of note when a ferromagnetic material is used. In this special case, an internal or intrinsic magnetization B_i exists in the material at all times. When an external magnetizing force is applied to a ferromagnetic material, the internal flux density does not increase indefinitely, but instead reaches a saturation level, as determined by the characteristics of the specific material. This is illustrated in Fig. 3-5(b). Summarizing then, the total magnetic flux density plotted in Fig. 3-4 is the resultant of a flux density present in any material regardless of type which is subjected to an applied H and an internal flux density present only in ferromagnetic materials. It may be expressed as

total flux density = permeability of vacuum × magnetizing force + internal flux density

or $$B = \mu_v H + B_i \text{ gauss} \tag{3-7}$$

where μ_v is the permeability of vacuum (gauss/oersted), H is the magnetizing force (oersted), and B_i is the internal flux density (gauss).

3-7. Hysteresis

Assume again that a wholly demagnetized specimen of ferromagnetic material is placed within a magnetizing coil. If the magnetizing field is varied from zero in a positive direction, the flux density in the specimen will increase as shown by the curve $0a$ in Fig. 3-6. This is

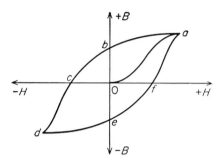

Fig. 3-6. Derivation of the static hysteresis curve.

the expected result, as described in Art. 3-6. However, if the magnetizing force is now decreased to zero, it is noted that the flux density follows the curve *ab*, Fig. 3-6. The *B-H* curve for the decreasing values of magnetizing force does not correspond with the original rising curve.

The flux density 0*b* remaining in the material after the magnetizing force has been returned to zero is called the *residual flux density,* and is determined by the *retentivity** of the material. If it is desired to remove the residual magnetism, that is, to move from point *b* to a zero value of *H*, a magnetizing force 0*c* must be applied in the reverse direction. This magnetizing force which removes the residual magnetism is called the *coercive force* or *coercive field,* and is a measure of the retentivity of the material.

If the magnetizing force is further increased in the negative direction, the flux density follows the curve *cd*. If the magnetizing force is returned to its zero value, and is then increased in the positive direction, the flux density follows the curve *defa* and the loop shown in Fig. 3-6 closes. At this point, the ferromagnetic material has been taken through a complete magnetic cycle.

Although it appears from this description of the *B-H* curve that a loop is formed after the value of *H* has been varied over one cycle (from zero to positive maximum *H*, to zero, to negative maximum *H*, to zero to positive maximum *H*), this is not completely correct. The loop does not close until the magnetizing force has been varied through several cycles, after which time the material may be considered to be cyclically magnetized. (Note that the original *B-H* curve 0*a* is not retraced; it can only be obtained if *H* is applied to the specimen in its wholly demagnetized state.)

The area under the *B-H* curve is called the *hysteresis loop* or *hysteresis curve* of the material. The term hysteresis — derived from the Greek *hysterein,* to be behind, to lag — refers to the fact that the

---

* Retentivity is the ability of a material to retain magnetic characteristics after the external magnetizing force is removed. Permanent magnets have a high degree of retentivity, while temporary magnets have a low value of retentivity.

flux density B lags behind the applied magnetizing force H, as evidenced by the hysteresis curve. In other words, the change in the magnetic state of the material lags behind the change in the magnetizing force, causing the descending portion of the curve (*abcd* in Fig. 3-6) to lie above the ascending portion (*defa*). The area inside the loop represents lost energy which is dissipated as heat.

A hysteresis curve formed by a magnetizing force that is varying *slowly* is called a *static* or *d-c* hysteresis loop. If, however, the cyclically varying magnetizing force is changing *rapidly*, the B-H curve formed is called a *dynamic* hysteresis loop. A distinction is made between these two types of curves since the core losses, described in Art. 3-8, increase and thus become important under dynamic operating conditions. The losses cause the dynamic hysteresis loop to be inherently wider than the static loop. In magnetic-amplifier circuitry, the dynamic hysteresis loop is all important for circuit analysis and in determining the performance of an amplifier in a given application.

The actual shape of the hysteresis curve is dependent upon several different factors. In the first place, the loop may be symmetrical, as shown in Fig. 3-6, or nonsymmetrical. The latter curve results when the magnitude of the positive maximum value of the magnetizing force does not equal the negative maximum excursion. The loop shape also reflects the characteristics of the core metal (the higher the permeability, the narrower the curve), the core lamination thickness (the thicker each lamination, the wider the loop), the frequency of the applied magnetizing force (the higher the frequency, the wider the loop), the temperature of the core (generally the higher the tempera-

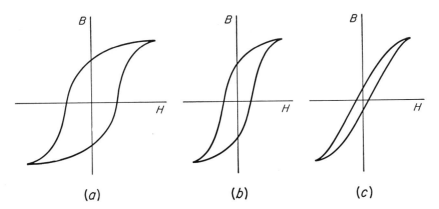

Fig. 3-7. Hysteresis loops of different shapes for (a) tungsten steel core, (b) mild steel core, and (c) stalloy core.

ture, the narrower the loop), and the amplitude of the applied magnetizing force (the greater the amplitude, the wider the loop). Typical curves of different widths are illustrated in Fig. 3-7.

3-8. Energy and power losses in ferromagnetic cores

The energy losses encountered in ferromagnetic cores are essentially of two major groups, hysteresis losses and eddy-current losses. *Hysteresis losses* result when a ferromagnetic material* is forced to change from one magnetic state to another, as it is when a varying magnetizing force is applied to it. Thus a magnetizing force of given direction will cause the core to assume certain specific magnetic polarities; reversing the direction of H causes the core to shift its poles. The hysteresis loss is, in effect, the work required to produce this shift. This loss may be noted as a heat loss in the core. As a result, only a portion of the energy absorbed by the ferromagnetic core when a magnetizing force is applied to it is returned when the force is removed. The difference between the energy absorbed and that restored is the hysteresis loss, and is proportional to the area under the hysteresis loop. Consequently, a tungsten steel core, with a curve as shown in Fig. 3-7(a), has a higher loss than a stalloy core, Fig. 3-7(c). The tungsten steel loss is so large as to make the material unsuited for magnetic applications when cyclically varying magnetic fields are encountered. It must be noted however that the high value of residual flux density of this material (or any material with a similar loop shape) makes it suitable for use as a permanent magnet.

In the case of mild steel, Fig. 3-7(b), its loop area is too large to permit it to be used in the presence of alternating magnetic fields, but too small to permit its use as a permanent magnet. However, the relatively high permeability of this material leads to its use for parts of machines subjected to a constant flux. The curve of stalloy, Fig. 3-7(c), shows that the material has a low hysteresis loss. This material, and similar ones, are used for armatures, transformer cores, and in all applications which require the material to operate under conditions of alternating magnetization.

A comparison of the three curves immediately indicates that a larger value of H is necessary to produce a given value of B in a wide

---

* There are no hysteresis losses in the cases of air and other nonmagnetic materials; all energy absorbed by these materials when a magnetizing force is applied is restored when the force is removed.

curve, Fig. 3-7(a). From this it necessarily follows that the losses must be greater as the area contained by the closed loop increases.

The second major power loss is the eddy-current loss. When the magnetic flux in a ferromagnetic core varies cyclically, or alternates, a voltage is induced into the core (see Art. 3-9) in much the same way as voltage is induced from primary to secondary of a transformer. This induced core voltage produces eddy currents in the core. The resulting I^2R losses are the eddy-current losses of the core. These losses, like those of hysteresis, represent the conversion of energy into heat which cannot be utilized. The sum of the two losses is the core loss.

Hysteresis losses may be minimized by proper selection of the core material. If it is chosen with characteristics of high permeability and low retentivity, the losses are low. Eddy-current losses may be decreased by laminating the core, i.e., constructing the core of thin metallic slices separated from each other by a thin layer of insulation. The eddy currents are thus isolated from each other; furthermore, the resistance of the long thin lamination is high, also decreasing the currents. Further reduction of this loss derives from selecting a core material of high electrical resistivity.

The core material selected for the magnetic amplifier should have certain distinct characteristics. For one, this material should have a square (or rectangular) B-H curve, approaching the ideal shown in Fig. 3-8(a). Although no material exists that will produce the idealized magnetization curve, many do have characteristics approaching it, as shown in Fig. 3-8(b), so that small variations in

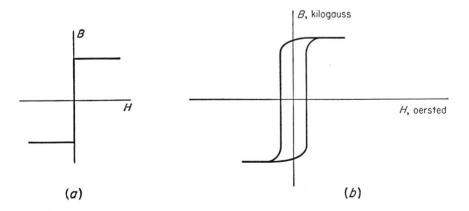

Fig. 3-8. Square or rectangular B-H curves of core materials: (a) idealized magnetization curve; (b) typical magnetization curve.

magnetizing force produce large linear variations in flux density. In addition, magnetic amplifier core materials should have the following properties:

    a. Low hysteresis and eddy-current losses. This may be obtained from materials having a high resistivity, a low coercive force, and the ability to be produced in thin laminations.

    b. High saturation flux density, B_s. This characteristic permits a given weight of core material to have a large power capacity, and is extremely important where low-weight units are required.

    c. Stability of magnetic characteristics under conditions of varying temperature and mechanical strain.

Some of the more common and useful core materials are listed in Table 3-2.

Table 3-2. Magnetic Amplifier Core Materials

Material	Commercial name	Nominal composition	Saturation flux density B_s (kilogauss)	Magnetizing force H_s (oersted) for B_s	Permeability (kilogauss/ oersted)
Silicon-iron alloy	Silectron Trancor Hipersil Corosil	97 Fe, 3 Si	19.7	800	60
Nickel-iron alloy	Deltamax Permenorm Orthonol	50 Ni, 50 Fe	15.5	15	125
	Nicaloi Hipernik Conpernik	49 Ni, 51 Fe	15.5	100	68
	Permalloy	65 Ni, 35 Fe	13.7	150	400
	Molypermalloy	79 Ni, 17 Fe, 4 Mo	8.8	25	80
	Mumetal	75 Ni, 18 Fe, 5 Cu, 2 Cr	6.7	50	105

The permeability of pure iron is greater than that of any other element, and, depending upon its degree of purity, may reach a value of 3.4×10^5. However, the addition of controlled quantities of impurities is useful for the production of certain definite characteristics in the material. The addition of between 2 and 4 per cent silicon to iron, as in the silicon-iron alloy, tends to remove oxygen and carbon, and results in a relatively soft magnetic alloy with high resistivity.

This alloy is of value when hysteresis and eddy-current losses should be held to a minimum, as in the core of power transformers and in rotating armatures.

In those applications where a transformer is to reproduce an input waveform faithfully, the core selected must have a magnetization curve with a linear relationship between B and H. For the core to have this characteristic, its permeability must be high and of fixed value over a wide range of magnetization; this means that the hysteresis loop must have but slight curvature and enclose only a small area. This is generally true in the nickel-iron alloys, as Permalloy, for example.

The alloys listed in Table 3-2 are all magnetically soft alloys. It must be realized, however, that many industrial applications require the use of an alloy with high retentivity and a large coercive force. These characteristics are desirable in permanent magnets. A magnetically hard alloy, consisting of iron, aluminum, nickel, and cobalt and called alnico, has these properties. Other alloys known as the *MK steels*, which consist of iron, nickel, and aluminum, also have high retentivities and large coercive forces.

The specific characteristics of any given material can be changed radically by such processing as *annealing* and *rolling*. In annealing a material, it is raised to a suitable temperature, usually between 700° and 1400°C, and then allowed to cool gradually. This heating process may be accomplished before or after the core material is stamped into its finished form, and may be carried out in a gaseous atmosphere (as in the presence of hydrogen) or under a magnetic field.

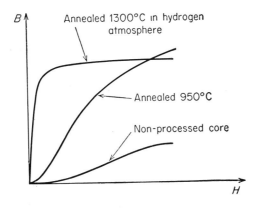

Fig. 3-9. Curves produced by annealing core materials.

The annealing process produces a marked improvement in the *B-H* curves of materials to be used as saturable reactor cores. This may be seen in Fig. 3-9. Note that the curve for the material annealed in a hydrogen atmosphere approaches the ideal curve.

Rolling the core material, that is, reducing it to its required thickness by mechanical rolling mills, may be accomplished either before or after annealing, depending upon the specific material under process. The rolling action can be performed with the material at normal or high temperatures. This process also improves the *B-H* curve and reduces the hysteresis losses.

3-9. Electromagnetic induction, Faraday's experiments

In the year 1831, Michael Faraday was observing the characteristics of, and experimenting with, the magnetic field produced by a current flowing in a conductor. During one of his experiments, he discovered that if a solenoid wound on a hollow form was connected to a galvanometer, the galvanometer would register when a bar magnet was moved into, or out of, the hollow form. (See Fig. 3-10.) If, however, the bar magnet was not in motion, no galvanometer deflection was observed. He further noted that the magnitude and direction of the galvanometer deflection were affected by: (1) the direction of magnet motion (the galvanometer needle would deflect in one direction when the magnet was moving into the coil, and in the opposite direction when the magnet was moving away from the coil); (2) the polarity of the magnet (the needle deflection produced when a north pole of the magnet was moved into the coil was opposite to that produced when the south pole was moved into the coil); and (3) the rate of speed with which the bar magnet moved in and out of the coil (the greater the rate of speed, the greater the galvanometer deflection).

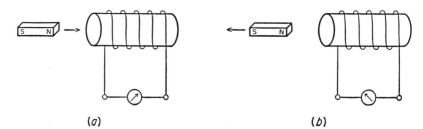

(a)   (b)

Fig. 3-10. Voltage induced into a coil cut by magnetic lines of force: (a) magnet moving into coil; (b) magnet moving away from coil.

In further experiments, Faraday also noticed that the same actions would occur if the bar magnet was held stationary but the coil was in motion.

Based upon these observations, the property of *electromagnetic induction* was formulated; namely, whenever magnetic lines of force cut, or are cut by, a conductor or a series of conductors, an electromotive force (or voltage) is induced into the conductor. The value of the induced electromotive force is governed by: (1) the total number of lines of force that cut, or are cut by, the coil; (2) the number of turns of wire in the coil; and (3) the rate of speed with which the lines of force are cut. The induced electromotive force is given by the equation

$$E = \frac{N\Phi}{t \times 10^8} \text{ volt} \tag{3-8}$$

where E = induced electromotive force in volts
  N = number of conductors cutting the magnetic flux
  Φ = total number of lines of force cutting the conductors
  t = time in seconds.

The factor of 10^8 is introduced so that Eq. (3-8) can be given in volts, since it has been shown that an electromotive force of one volt is induced when 10^8 lines of force are cut in one second.

3-10. Direction of induced electromotive force, Lenz's law

The German physicist Lenz made further investigations into the characteristics of electromagnetic induction and discovered that a fixed relationship always exists between the induced electromotive force and the force producing it. Lenz's law may be summarized by stating that the direction of an induced electromotive force is always such as to oppose the change producing it.

This law may be understood by observing Fig. 3-11. In (a), the bar magnet is moving into the coil. The emf induced in the coil produces an electron flow, and the coil acts as an electromagnet, with polarity as shown. Note that the coil's north pole is in direct opposition to the pole of the bar magnet closest to it, thus repelling the change producing the induced electromotive force. In other words, the flux set up around the coil by the induced emf acts to prevent entry of the bar magnet into the coil. In (b), the bar magnet is moving away from the coil. The polarity of the coil now is such that its south

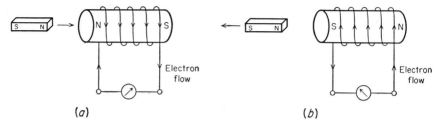

Fig. 3-11. Lenz's law: induced electromotive force sets up a magnetic field opposing the change which produced it. (a) Magnet moving into coil; (b) magnet moving away from coil.

pole is close to the north pole of the bar magnet. The force of attraction so produced acts to prevent the bar magnet from leaving the coil.

The general expression for induced electromotive force given in Eq. (3-8) is shown frequently with a negative (−) sign preceding the right-hand number. The negative sign indicates that the direction of the induced emf is such as to oppose the change.

3-11. Self-induction and inductance

As described in Art. 3-9, an induced electromotive force appears in a conductor which cuts, or is cut by, magnetic lines of force. If, now, the situation is considered when a coil or conductor is connected through a switch to a source of voltage, the property of *self-induction* may be observed. When the switch is open, no current flows in the coil, and no magnetic flux is set up around it, Fig. 3-12(a). When the switch is closed, current flows in the coil, and a magnetic field is built up around the coil, Fig. 3-12(b). During this build-up, the flux cuts the conductors of the coil, satisfying the conditions necessary for

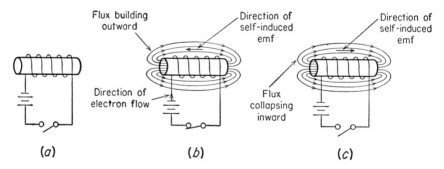

Fig. 3-12. Self-induction in a coil. (a) Switch open; (b) switch closed; (c) switch reopened.

electromagnetic induction. As a result, an electromotive force is induced into the coil itself by the increasing magnetic field building up around the coil. This is self-induction. The direction of the induced emf follows Lenz's law, and opposes the change that produced it, which is, in this case, the rise in current in the conductor. Thus, the counter emf delays the growth of current in the circuit, so that it takes a finite time to reach its final value. When the current finally levels off, the magnetic flux around the coil is steady, and electromagnetic self-induction no longer occurs.

When the switch is now opened, the circuit current falls to zero, and the magnetic flux collapses into the coil, Fig. 3-12(c). Again self-induction occurs, and the induced emf once more tends to oppose the change producing it. The direction of this induced emf (which is opposite to that produced when the switch was originally closed and the field building up) acts as to maintain the current flow in the circuit. Thus, the energy that is stored in the magnetic field when the field is building up initially is returned to the circuit when the field is collapsing.

The coil described, in which the self-induced emf appeared, is said to possess the property of *inductance*. Inductance is the property of a circuit which tends to oppose any change in current. Thus, if current is increasing in a circuit, the circuit inductance sets up a counter emf which opposes the current increase; if current is decreasing, the circuit inductance sets up an induced emf which opposes the current decrease.

The value of inductance of a coil is determined by its physical specifications; namely, the turns of wire in the coil, the spacing between turns, and the permeability of the core. The unit of inductance is the *henry;* a coil has an inductance of one henry when a current of one ampere produces 10^8 linkages between flux and coil. In a one-henry coil, an emf of one volt is induced by a current changing at the rate of one ampere per second. The inductance of a coil is

$$L = \frac{N\Phi}{I \times 10^8} \text{ henry} \tag{3-9}$$

where L = inductance in henries
N = number of conductors linked by magnetic flux
Φ = total number of flux linkages
I = current producing the magnetic flux, in amperes.

From this equation, it can be seen that the inductance is proportional to $N\Phi$, which is a measure of the total flux linkage in the circuit.

Thus, any physical change made to a coil which would increase its flux linkage would increase the coil inductance. In the case of the coil characteristics previously specified, the inductance would be increased if:

(1) A greater number of turns of wire were added to the coil.
(2) The spacing between adjacent turns were decreased.
(3) A core of high permeability were used.

For a solenoid, the empirical formula for its inductance is

$$L = \frac{1.26 N^2 \mu A}{l \times 10^8} \text{ henry} \tag{3-10}$$

where L = inductance in henries
N = number of turns in the solenoid
μ = permeability of the core
A = area of the core in square centimeters
l = length of the core in square centimeters.

Although this formula can be used for calculating the inductance of a solenoid, its primary use at this point is in illustrating the factors that determine the inductance of a coil. From the formula, it can be seen that the inductance is proportional to the core permeability and core area and to the square of the number of turns in the coil, but is inversely proportional to the length of the core.

3-12. Inductive reactance

As described above, inductance of a coil opposes any change in current. However, the actual current-limiting value of the coil in the presence of alternating current is dependent upon the frequency of the alternating source and the inductance of the coil. This effect of the coil, which limits the flow of alternating current, is called its inductive reactance, and is measured in ohms. (No inductive reactance is established by the coil in the presence of a pure direct current, since no relative motion exists between the magnetic flux and the coil.)

The inductive reactance of a circuit is given as follows:

$$X_L = 2\pi f L \tag{3-11}$$

where X_L = inductive reactance in ohms
F = frequency of the supply voltage in cycles per second
L = inductance of the circuit in henries.

The introduction of inductive reactance into a circuit offers an opposition to the current flowing in the circuit, and results in the current being lower than it would be if no inductance were present. In a pure inductive circuit, the current in the circuit may be determined by the a-c Ohm's law in the following manner:

$$I = \frac{E}{X_L} \qquad (3\text{-}12)$$

where I = current in amperes
E = emf of the source voltage in volts
X_L = inductive reactance in ohms.

Because of the opposition offered to the applied voltage by the inductive reactance, the current in an inductive circuit always lags the voltage by a phase angle of between 0 and 90 degrees. In a pure inductive circuit — one in which there is no resistance — the angle of lag is 90 degrees. In a pure resistive circuit, the angle of lag is 0 degree.

In a circuit containing both resistance and inductance, the total opposition to current is a vector quantity called the *impedance*, Z. In an *R-L* circuit, the impedance is

$$Z = \sqrt{R^2 + X_L^2} \qquad (3\text{-}13)$$

where Z = total impedance in ohms
R = resistance of the circuit in ohms
X_L = inductive reactance of the circuit in ohms.

The circuit current in an *R-L* circuit is $I = E/Z$.*

3-13. Mutual induction

The electromagnetic induction produced in a coil by the field building up and collapsing around the coil itself is called self-induction. The electromagnetic induction which occurs between two mutually independent circuits is called *mutual induction*. Mutual induction occurs when two coils are placed adjacent to each other such that a change in one causes a magnetic field to cut the conductors of the second, thereby inducing a voltage into the second. The coil that receives the initial power from the voltage source is called the primary winding, while the other is called the secondary.

The mutual inductance existing between two coils is given as

$$M = k\sqrt{L_1 \times L_2} \qquad (3\text{-}14)$$

---

* Students requiring a review of the fundamentals of a-c theory, touched upon only briefly in this article, should consult a textbook on the subject.

where M = mutual inductance in henries
  L_1 = inductance of one coil in henries
  L_2 = inductance of second coil in henries
  k = coefficient of coupling between the coils.

The coefficient of coupling, expressed as a decimal, is the ratio between the number of lines of flux cutting the second coil and the number of lines of force produced by the primary winding. If all of the lines of force around the primary cut the secondary, then unity coupling exists and $k = 1$. If only 40 per cent of the lines produced by the primary cut the secondary, then $k = 0.4$.

The transformer represents the most common application of the characteristic of mutual induction. In the case of a power transformer, for example, the primary and secondary windings are placed on a common iron core, as shown in Fig. 3-13. When source voltage is applied to the primary so that current flows through the primary, magnetic lines of force are produced around the primary. Most of the lines of force are concentrated in the core (Fig. 3-13) and link the

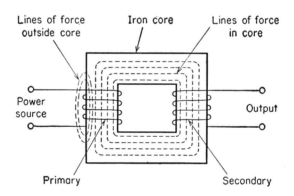

Fig. 3-13. The fundamental power transformer as an example of mutual induction.

secondary winding. If the power source produces a variable current in the primary, an induced voltage will appear in the secondary, attributed to mutual induction. The few lines of force which are outside the core of Fig. 3-13 prevent unity coupling in the power transformer. Despite this leakage, however, the coefficient of coupling in transformers of this type may be as high as 0.98.

REVIEW QUESTIONS

1. An electromagnet is required to produce a magnetomotive force F of 628 gilberts for a specific industrial application. (a) How many ampere turns must the coil have to produce this force? (Assume $\pi = 3.14$.) (b) If the coil has 500 turns of conductor, how much current is required?

2. What magnetomotive force results when 5 milliamperes of current pass through 800 turns of wire?

3. An electromagnet consists of 1500 turns of wire wound on a core which has a length of 15 cm. If it is assumed that the magnetic circuit length is identical to the core length, what is the magnetizing force produced when 50 milliamperes of current flow in the electromagnet?

4. What is the flux density in kilogausses of a magnet which has a uniform flux of 100,000 maxwells over an area of 5 cm by 4 cm?

5. What must be the cross-sectional area of a magnet which has a magnet flux of 500,000 maxwells and a flux density of 20 kilogausses?

6. What is the permeability of a medium which has a flux density of 20 kilogausses and a magnetizing force of 15,000 oersteds?

7. If the permeability of a medium is 12.5, a magnetizing force of 25,000 oersteds will produce a flux density of what value?

8. A coil having 200 turns is linked by a flux of 4,000,000 lines. The flux strength decreases from maximum to zero in 0.05 sec. How much voltage is induced into the coil?

9. Define the term *inductance*.

10. What is the inductance of a solenoid which has 250 turns of wire wound on a circular cardboard tube 2 cm in diameter and 12 cm long? (The permeability of cardboard, a nonmagnetic material, is 1.)

11. An inductance of 50 millihenries is placed in series with a 20-v, 500-kc a-c signal. (a) What is its inductive reactance? (b) How much current will flow through the coil?

4

The Saturable Reactor

4-1. General

The terms *saturable reactor* and *magnetic amplifier* are used frequently in today's literature in a confusing and contradictory manner. To prevent such confusion in this text, the devices are described as follows: a *magnetic amplifier* is a circuit device consisting of combinations of saturable reactors, rectifiers, resistors, and conventional transformers used to secure control or amplification; a *saturable reactor* (or transductor) is the reactor alone regardless of how it is used.

The saturable reactor (sometimes called the saturable-core reactor) is the prime component common to all magnetic amplifiers; consequently, it is described in theory and operation prior to the magnetic amplifier.

4-2. Introduction to the saturable reactor

The simplest saturable reactor consists of a single ferromagnetic core (either rectangular or circular) having two windings, namely, an *a-c coil* or *load winding* N_L and a *d-c* or *control winding* N_C. This reactor is shown in Fig. 4-1(a). For circuit operation, the control winding is

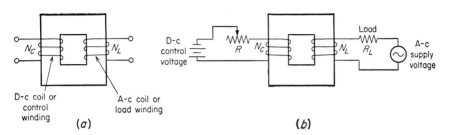

Fig. 4-1. (a) Simplest saturable reactor. (b) Simple saturable reactor connected in circuit.

connected to a source of d-c control voltage and the load winding is connected in series with the load and a supply of a-c voltage, as in Fig. 4-1(b). When the current is varied, the impedance of the load winding is changed, thereby determining the voltage output appearing across the load. One of the problems existing in the fundamental reactor of Fig. 4-1 is that the mutual induction between the d-c and a-c windings causes interaction between the control and load circuits.

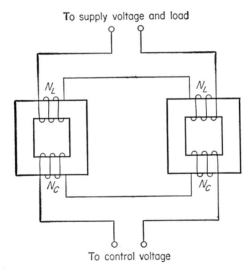

Fig. 4-2. Saturable reactor having two cores to reduce mutual induction.

The slightly more sophisticated reactor shown in Fig. 4-2(a), having two separate core elements with series control and series load windings, causes the induced voltages to cancel, thereby reducing the unwanted effects.

The most common basic saturable reactor consists of a three-legged closed laminated core, with coils wound on each leg. The core

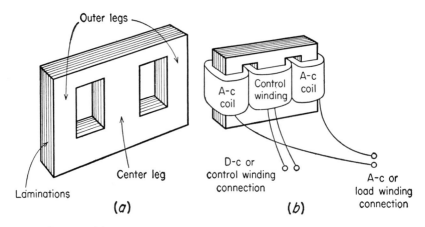

Fig. 4-3. (a) Three-legged closed saturable reactor core. (b) Coils wound on saturable reactor core.

is shown in Fig. 4-3(a); note that the center leg may be approximately twice as wide as either of the outer legs. Two coils having an equal number of turns are wound on the outer legs [Fig. 4-3(b)]; these are the *a-c coils* or the *load windings* (N_L). The coil on the middle leg usually has many more turns of wire than the outer coils; it is referred to as the *d-c* or *control winding* (N_C). The three-legged saturable reactor may be represented schematically by the appropriate symbol illustrated in Fig. 4-4. Graphical and schematic symbols* for reactors of several different types are included for comparison in this figure. Although the symbols for the twin-ring and three-legged cores show the load and control windings as connected in series aiding, this is not necessarily so. As described later in the text, these windings may be connected in series opposing or in parallel according to the specific application.

In order to understand the operation of the saturable reactor, consider first the simple circuit of Fig. 4-5(a), which shows a single coil N_C wound on a ferromagnetic core and supplied with current from a d-c source. When the switch is closed, varying the rheostat controls the current flowing through the coil, in turn controlling the degree of magnetization in the core. As shown in Fig. 4-5(b), an increase in coil current produces an increase in flux density until core saturation is approached. From this point on, further current increases do not affect the flux density appreciably. This curve is, of course, a represen-

---

* Graphical and schematic symbols will be used interchangeably throughout this text.

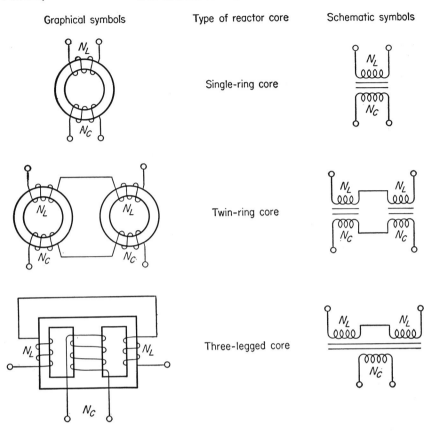

Fig. 4-4. Graphical and schematic symbols of winding arrangements of some saturable reactors. *Notes:* (a) Ring cores may be shown graphically as square or circular. (b) Load windings N_L and/or control windings N_C are shown connected in series aiding, but according to application may be connected in series opposing or in parallel.

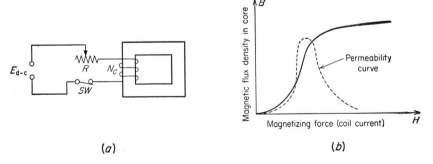

Fig. 4-5. (a) Controlling the current in an iron-core inductance. (b) Core magnetization plotted against coil current.

tation of the steady-state conditions observable when a d-c voltage is used as the source.

Assume now that a second coil N_L is wound on the core [Fig. 4-6(a) and (b)] and is supplied voltage by an a-c source. If the switch SW in the primary N_C circuit is opened, the current flowing in the N_L winding is determined (neglecting resistance R_L for the

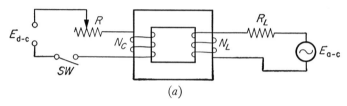

(a)

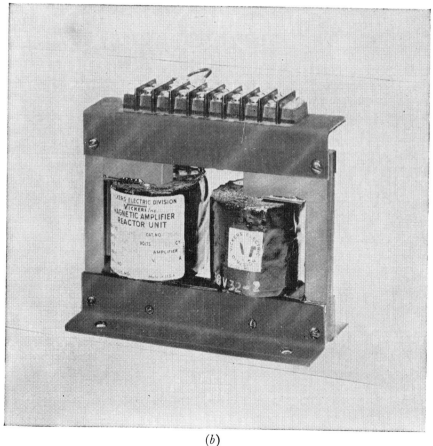

(b)

Fig. 4-6. (a) Basic saturable reactor circuit. (b) Saturable reactor, cover moved. (*Courtesy, Vickers Electric Division.*)

present) by the circuit's inductive reactance X_L and the applied voltage $E_{a\text{-}c}$, as given in Eq. (3-12). The inductance of a coil was defined earlier as the number of flux linkages per ampere of current producing the flux, or

$$L = \frac{N\Phi}{I} \times 10^{-8} \text{ henry} \qquad (3\text{-}9)$$

where N is the number of turns in the coil and Φ, in maxwells, is the magnetic flux linked with them due to the current I, in amperes.* Since the flux density B is proportional to the magnetic flux Φ [Eq. (3-4)], it becomes evident with reference to Eq. (3-9) that the inductance is proportional to the permeability μ of the core, defined previously as the ratio between flux density B and magnetizing force H [Eq. (3-5)].

The permeability of a ferromagnetic core is not constant, but varies depending upon the portion of the $B\text{-}H$ curve that is examined. Thus, referring to the dashed curve of Fig. 4-5(b), the permeability is large for small values of magnetizing forces, rises to a peak for moderate values of H, and decreases for larger values of H. At saturation, the permeability reaches its lowest value. As a consequence, the inductance of a coil is not constant; it, too, decreases as the $B\text{-}H$ curve approaches saturation.

How are these facts applied to an explanation of the basic saturable circuit of Fig. 4-6(a)? Assume that no d-c current is allowed to flow in the N_C winding of the reactor so that this control winding produces no magnetic flux in the core. The total flux, then, is that produced by only the a-c current flowing in the N_L winding; this current is determined by $I_L = E_{a\text{-}c}/\sqrt{R_L{}^2 + X_L{}^2}$. The applied voltage $E_{a\text{-}c}$ divides between X_L and R_L in a manner governed by the magnitudes of their respective impedances. With no direct current flowing in the N_C winding, the control winding contributes no flux to the core, and the total flux, produced by the alternating current only, is considerably less than magnetic core saturation. As a result, the permeability of the core and the inductance and inductive reactance of the coil are high, and a larger percentage of the applied voltage $E_{a\text{-}c}$ appears across X_L than across R_L.

---

* It is true that the flux linking the turns in a coil can be computed only for the very simplest cases. In actuality, the formulas for the commonly used coils are complicated functions of their dimensions.

If, now, a direct current is permitted to flow in the N_C winding of the reactor, it will set up a magnetic flux and in effect will determine the state of magnetization of the core. The total flux now produced will be the sum of the fluxes contributed by both the N_C and N_L windings. Because circuit operation is now being accomplished for larger values of magnetizing force, the permeability of the core, and consequently the inductance and inductive reactance of the coil, are decreased. As a result, the percentage of the applied voltage E_{a-c} appearing across X_L decreases and that across R_L increases. This action then indicates that the direct current in the N_C winding is the control current. It determines the state of the core, thus setting the level of inductance of the coil N_L. By adjusting this control current, the voltage applied to the load R_L can be varied over a wide range of values.

4-3. Fundamental saturable-reactor circuit

The first practical saturable-reactor circuit, similar to that shown in Fig. 4-6(a), was described in 1901 by C. F. Burgess and B. Frankenfield. In this basic circuit, the saturable reactor has a single core and two windings [see Fig. 4-6(a)]. The control winding N_C is supplied with direct current from a d-c supply with magnitude determined by the rheostat R. The load winding N_L is in series with the load R_L and is supplied by an a-c source. In this fundamental circuit, the impedance of the load winding is determined by the direct current flowing in the control winding. When the direct current is at its minimum value, as determined by the maximum resistance of R, the inductive reactance of N_L is maximum and the load current I_L is minimum. The a-c voltage developed across the load is at its lowest value at this time. As the resistance R is decreased so that the current I_C in the control circuit increases, the impedance of the load winding is reduced accordingly, and load current I_L increases. The load voltage thus increases as the d-c magnetization of the reactor increases. At core saturation, the impedance of N_L reaches its lowest value, and the load voltage rises to its peak.

In this circuit operation, then, the saturable reactor functions as a d-c controlled inductive series impedance. The function of the basic circuit, as described in the patent application by Burgess and Frankenfield,* is to supply "a method of regulating and controlling the current

---

* United States Patent 720,844.

and potential in an electric circuit or system of circuits whereby
. . . smooth and uniform variations in the circuit are obtained
for the purposes of regulation."

The basic reactor circuit can be used to vary large a-c load voltages
slowly and smoothly, and with a wide range of control, as for groups of
lamps used for theatre lighting or display, or for electric heaters in
industrial furnaces. Thus, a small variable resistor of low voltage can
be used to provide control over a large a-c power. The power gain of
this elementary non-feedback circuit, as determined by output power
$I_L{}^2R_L$ divided by input power $I_C{}^2R_C$, ranges between 5 and 125, and
depends primarily on the design of the saturable-core reactor in the
circuit.

As a further explanation of the basic reactor operation, consider
the magnetization curve of Fig. 4-7. Assume that the current in the
d-c control winding creates a magnetizing force in the core of 0.2
oersted, setting the operating state of the curve to point O. If the
magnetizing force of the a-c source is represented by the sine wave

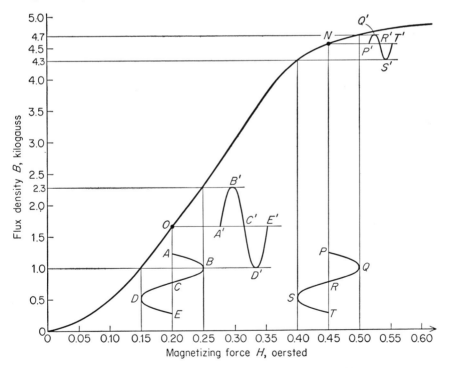

Fig. 4-7. Graphical representation of operation of basic saturable-reactor
circuit.

ABCDE (a total variation in *H* of 0.1 oersted), the resulting flux density, represented by the curve *A'B'C'D'E'*, varies between 1 and 2.3 kilogausses. This large variation in a-c flux density means that the number of flux linkages is large, the inductive reactance of the a-c coil is high, and the a-c voltage dropped across the coil is large with respect to that across the load R_L.

Assume now that the direct current is increased to produce a magnetizing force of 0.45 oersted so that the *B-H* curve is operating at point *N*. If the magnetizing force of the a-c source is represented by sine wave *PQRST* (a total variation in *H* of 0.1 oersted, like that of sine wave *ABCDE*), the resulting flux density, as shown by *P'Q'R'S'T'*, varies only between 4.3 and 4.7 kilogausses, a variation of but 0.4 kilogauss. This decreased variation in flux density means that the amplitude of the voltage across the coil is decreased, while that of the load is increased.

This, then, is the action of the saturable reactor. Small changes in control current vary the magnetization state of the ferromagnetic core over wide limits, thus permitting the control of relatively large powers. Although some power is dissipated in the control winding because of I^2R losses, the power gain (ratio of controlled output power to control power) obtainable with the basic circuit ranges from a few thousand to several million.

4-4. Saturable reactor characteristics

As mentioned in the previous chapter, the *B-H* curve for any specified ferromagnetic core does not follow a simple law, nor can a simple mathematical expression be derived readily to represent its shape. Although it is true that a complex expression can be formulated to represent the curve, its value is limited since many of the characteristics of the saturable reactor can best be obtained under test in the laboratory. However, it is normal practice to discuss the reactor with respect to an idealized curve, one example of which was illustrated in Fig. 3-8(a). Three additional idealized curves are shown in Fig. 4-8. The section of each simplified curve labeled 0-1 represents a high permeability; the 1-2 section corresponds to the interval during which a magnetic core saturation is approached or reached. The 0-3-4 section represents the curve plotted during the interval when the magnetizing force is reversed (as when the coil current is reversed). The idealized curve represents the core as producing a mirror-image result of the reversal. Although this is not quite correct, it is sufficient-ly valid for this discussion.

Figure 4-8(a) illustrates a situation in which the flux density of the core rises sharply and steadily as the magnetization force (proportional to the product of the number of turns in a coil and the magnetizing current through the coil) increases. At point 1, the core saturates completely, and the permeability decreases to zero value. A further increase in H has no effect on B. The curve of Fig. 4-8(b) has the same initial section as that of (a), but illustrates a condition in which saturation is approached gradually, rather than suddenly. The curve of Fig. 4-8(c) represents a core material with a permeability that is infinite over the initial portion of the B-H curve, but whose permeabil-ity decreases to a low value in the saturation region.

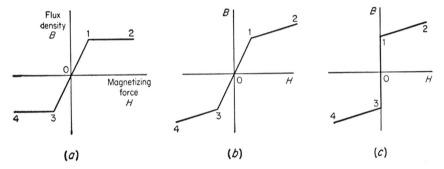

Fig. 4-8. Three simplified forms of idealized B-H curve.

In actuality, the selection of the particular form of the curve for any discussion of reactor characteristics is not of prime importance. As a rule, it is chosen by comparison with the characteristics of the core under analysis. Because most ferromagnetic cores have curves that approach that of Fig. 4-8(a), the remaining paragraphs of this section shall refer to a curve and a core of this type.

Consider then the curve of Fig. 4-9(a), an expanded version of Fig. 4-8(a), to which arbitrary values of B and H have been assigned. If it is assumed that no direct current is flowing in the control winding of the saturable reactor, so that this winding is contributing nothing to the magnetic state of the core, the magnetizing force produced by the alternating current applied to the a-c winding will alternate about the origin of the curve. Thus, if the force H swings between $+0.5$ and -0.5 oersted, the flux density will vary between $+3$ and -3 kilo-gauss. The permeability μ of the core (which is, in effect, the slope of

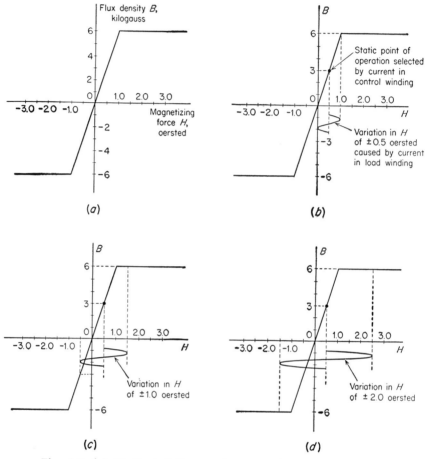

Fig. 4-9. (a) Idealized *B-H* curve for computing saturable reactor characteristics. (b) (c) (d) Operating characteristics of idealized curve.

the curve) is the ratio between B and H. For the example, μ equals 6000/1, or 6000.

If the current flowing in the a-c winding is increased so that the magnetizing force fluctuates between $+1.0$ and -1.0 oersted, the flux density shows a total excursion of 12 kilogausses. The permeability is 12,000/2, or 6000. Consequently, for all values of H up to and including ± 1 oersted, the permeability of the core is constant. This is necessarily true since the action is occurring only over the linear section of the curve.

Assume now that the a-c magnetizing force is varied between $+2$ and -2 oersted. For that portion of operation between $+1.0$ and -1.0 oersted, the permeability remains constant, as described above.

However, for magnetizing forces in the region between $+1.0$ and $+2.0$ oersted, and -1.0 and -2.0 oersted, the core is operating at saturation, and the permeability decreases to zero. The over-all flux density varies between $+6$ and -6 kilogauss, and the apparent over-all permeability is $12,000/4$ or 3000. (The apparent over-all permeability, which is used here to simplify the problem, is taken over the entire region of operation; the actual permeability would be taken on a point-to-point basis.) Further, if H is varied between ±3.0 oersted, B will continue to vary between $+6$ and -6 kilogauss, and the apparent permeability will decrease to 2000.

Table 4-1 summarizes these results. Note that with no d-c flowing in the control winding, the permeability remains fixed for low values of H, but decreases as H moves into the saturation portion of the curve.

Table 4-1. Characteristics of a Saturable Reactor

Magnetizing force H in oersteds produced by d-c in control winding	Magnetizing force H in oersteds produced by a-c (peak swing)	Total H (peak-to-peak)	Total flux density B in kilogausses (peak-to-peak)	Apparent over-all permeability (B/H)
0	0.5	1.0	6.0	6000
0	1.0	2.0	12.0	6000
0	2.0	4.0	12.0	3000
0	3.0	6.0	12.0	2000
0.5	0.5	1.0	6.0	6000
0.5	1.0	2.0	9.0	4500
0.5	2.0	4.0	12.0	3000
0.5	3.0	6.0	12.0	2000
1.0	0.5	1.0	3.0	3000
1.0	1.0	2.0	6.0	3000
1.0	2.0	4.0	12.0	3000
1.0	3.0	6.0	12.0	2000
2.0	1.0	2.0	0	0
2.0	2.0	4.0	6.0	1500
2.0	3.0	6.0	12.0	2000
2.0	4.0	8.0	12.0	1500

What does this mean with respect to the voltage developed across the a-c winding of the saturable reactor? The inductance of a coil is proportional to its permeability; the voltage developed across the coil is proportional to its inductance. For high values of permeability and low values of total magnetizing force, the voltage across the inductance is proportional to the magnetizing current. When magnetic saturation is approached, and the permeability is decreased, further increases in magnetizing force do not produce any increases in this voltage. Thus the average voltage across the a-c coil of a saturable reactor quickly reaches a maximum value and thereafter remains constant. (The actual voltage developed across the a-c coil of the saturable reactor will not be sinusoidal; when operating within the region of core saturation, the voltage developed across an ideal coil is zero.)

The action described assumed that no direct current was flowing in the control winding of the saturable reactor. Now consider its operation in the presence of a direct current, sometimes called a polarizing current, in the control winding. Assume that a current flows in the control winding so as to produce a steady magnetizing force of 0.5 oersted, which corresponds to a flux density of 3 kilogausses [Fig. 4-9(b)]. This, then, is the steady-operating point on the *B-H* curve. If now an a-c voltage is applied to the a-c winding of the reactor so as to contribute a magnetizing force of ±0.5 oersted, the flux density rises to +6 kilogausses on the positive swing, and decreases to 0 kilogauss on the negative. For values of a-c magnetizing force of 1, 2, or 3 oersteds, the positive swings drive the coil into magnetic saturation; for swings of 2 and 3 oersteds, saturation is also reached on the negative swings. See Fig. 4-9(c) and (d). These figures are also summarized in Table 4-1. Note that under these conditions the permeability of the core decreases rapidly, while the voltage across the coil increases more gradually to its maximum value.

Similar conditions result when the d-c magnetizing force is 1 and 2 oersteds, as shown in the table. For the 1-oersted state, the permeability is low, and the voltage across the a-c winding varies over a wide range. For the 2-oersted state, a permeability of zero is encountered, since the core, for certain values of a-c magnetizing force, remains within the saturation region of the curve.

The series of characteristics obtained from this table are, of course, based upon an idealized *B-H* curve. Despite this, they are typical of the saturable reactor. The characteristics of an actual core material show a strong similarity to those obtained from the idealized curve.

4-5. Basic saturable reactor circuits

In the basic saturable-reactor circuit of Fig. 4-6(a), the direct current through the control winding N_C determined the voltage variations across resistor R_L. As a simple example of the possible application of this circuit, assume that R_L is replaced by a large bank of theatre lights. The circuit permits the room lighting to be varied smoothly and economically by relatively small variations of d-c through the control winding. Other uses of the basic circuit are in temperature control systems, voltage and frequency regulators, radio-frequency modulators, and phase shifters.

This basic circuit does have certain definite disadvantages, however. A primary one is that the a-c applied across the load winding N_L will cause an a-c voltage to be induced into the control winding. Since this latter winding is of low impedance, large currents will flow in this winding, dissipating an appreciable amount of power. One method of minimizing this disadvantage is to place an iron-cored choke in series with the control winding.* The choke offers a low resistance to the direct current flowing in the control winding, but presents a high impedance to the fundamental-frequency induced currents and to all harmonics, thus limiting their amplitude. In this manner, the unwanted dissipation of power is reduced.

The series-impedance solution is, of course, the obvious one. However, it is of value only in those cases where the control current is unidirectional. In applications where the control voltage is a signal picked off some point in a circuit under control, the use of a choke is undesirable as it would limit the control winding voltage variations. To prevent this, the saturable reactor may be designed so that it is divided into two equal sections, and the control windings connected so that they are in series opposition, as illustrated in Fig. 4-10. For the

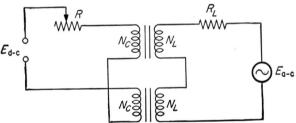

Fig. 4-10. Two-section saturable reactor with series-opposing control winding.

---

* A series high impedance is used in magnetic amplifiers which utilize feedback, and permits the N_L/N_C ratio to be of high value (from about 10 to 100). This means that a small number of turns in the control winding can be used to control the effects produced by a large number of load-winding turns, thus leading to a high power gain. Feedback amplifiers and their application will be discussed in later chapters.

core, the degree of saturation is not dependent upon the direction of the control windings; thus the d-c circuit operates properly in the presence of the series opposing windings. However, because the control windings are in opposite direction, any voltage induced into one by an alternating voltage in the load winding will be canceled by an equal and opposite voltage induced into the other. Thus, unwanted circulating currents will not appear in the control circuit, and yet no choke is present to impede any control signals applied to the control winding.

Although the circuit of Fig. 4-10 indicates one possible solution to the problem of unwanted a-c voltages in the control circuit, this is not the only solution. In reality, it makes little difference whether the d-c windings are connected in series opposition and the a-c windings in series aiding, as described here, or whether the d-c windings are con-

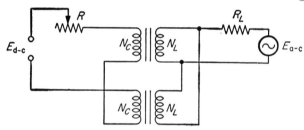

Fig. 4-11. Two-section saturable reactor with parallel-connected a-c windings.

nected in series aiding and the a-c windings in series opposing. The results in this latter case are also satisfactory. Furthermore, it is also possible for the a-c windings to be connected in parallel, Fig. 4-11, if it is so desired for a particular set of circuit conditions, such as in power applications where heavy currents are encountered.

In the twin-core arrangements, the problem of insulation between adjacent cores becomes important when the N_L/N_C is high. The coil voltages encountered necessitate a high degree of insulation, which requires a large space. Thus the twin-core reactors are normally used in magnetic-amplifier circuits having a low N_L/N_C ratio. It must be emphasized at this point, however, that it is never feasible for the divided d-c windings to be connected in parallel. If this were done, the unwanted voltage induced into the control windings would be additive, resulting in heavy circulating currents and excessive power dissipation in the windings.

In the symmetrical circuits described thus far (and in the case of the three-legged reactor that follows), the circuit arrangements are such as to reduce or eliminate only currents at the fundamental frequency, namely, the frequency of the a-c supply. However, since a core magnetization curve is not perfectly linear, harmonic components are also induced into the control windings. These do not necessarily cancel out. They may be reduced by the use of a choke in series with the control winding, or by specially selected filter networks. In twin-core reactors, only the fundamental frequency and odd harmonics of it appear in the load coil circuits, while even harmonics may be present in the control winding.

4-6. Three-legged saturable reactor

The double-sectional saturable reactor described in the preceding article is not commonly found in industry. The most common device

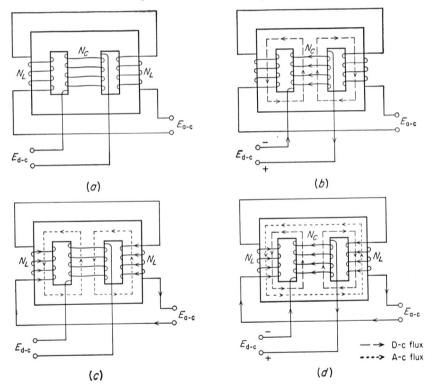

Fig. 4-12. (a) Three-legged saturable reactor with a-c coils connected in series aiding. (b) Magnetic flux produced by control winding alone. (c) Magnetic flux produced by a-c coils alone. (d) Total magnetic flux produced in three-legged saturable reactor. *Note:* In (c) and (d) the flux for only one half of the a-c cycle is illustrated.

utilizes a three-legged core with the a-c coils wound on the outer legs (connected either in series or parallel according to the requirements) and the control winding placed on the inner leg (Fig. 4-3). An electrical representation of a three-legged reactor with a-c coils connected in series is shown in Fig. 4-12(a). To understand its internal functioning, consider the core at the times when d-c is applied to the control winding, but a-c is not applied to the a-c coils. Under these conditions, and with the d-c polarity as indicated in Fig. 4-12(b), note that the magnetic flux (as represented by the dashed arrows) passes downward through the two outer legs, and upward through the center leg. The flux through the two outer legs is of equal intensity. If the d-c control polarity is reversed, the direction of the flux is reversed, but nothing else changes. Thus, with d-c applied to the control winding, the magnetic flux passes through each leg of the core, and core saturation can be obtained.

Assume now that no d-c is applied to the control winding, but that an a-c voltage of polarity indicated in Fig. 4-12(c) is applied to the a-c coils. The direction of magnetic flux (represented by the dotted arrows) is downward through the coil wound on the left leg, and upward through the coil on the right. These flux strengths are opposite and equal, and are relatively independent of one another. Consider now the condition of flux, as produced by the a-c coils, in the center leg of the core. In this leg the flux direction as produced by the right coil, is downward, and that produced by the left coil is upward. Since these fluxes are equal and opposite, they effectively cancel each other. In reality then, no flux is produced in the center core by the a-c flowing in the load coils. Rather, the flux lines of the two outer coils may be considered as joining in a common path through the outer core legs. This means, of course, that so far as the impedance of the a-c coils is concerned, the center core leg does not enter the picture.

Consider finally the action of the saturable reactor when d-c is applied to the control winding and a-c to the load windings, Fig. 4-12(d). The flux through the center leg is produced by the d-c control current; the flux through the outer legs is the resultant of that produced by both the control and load windings. On the a-c half-cycle when the polarity is as shown in Fig. 4-12(d), and the a-c voltage is at its peak value, the flux is large in the outer left core (the fluxes are additive) but small in the right core (the fluxes are opposing). It will be recalled that the impedance of a coil is determined by the rate of change in the magnetic flux in its core, rather than by the flux strength. Thus the impedance of the left coil is low and that of the right is high. The total impedance is the sum of the two coil impedances, since the a-c windings of this reactor are connected in series aiding. On the next a-c half-cycle, the a-c polarities reverse but the total impedance remains constant. In order to decrease the impedance, the amount of direct current must be increased. As core saturation is approached, the rate of change in magnetic flux decreases, and the impedance decreases.

As indicated previously, the a-c coils may, on occasion, be connected in parallel rather than in series. This is shown in Fig. 4-13.

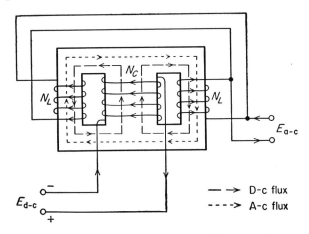

Fig. 4-13. Three-legged saturable reactor with a-c coils connected in parallel. *Note:* The flux for only one half of the a-c cycle is shown.

The action of the reactor is similar to that described for the series connection. One difference, however, is in the time response to a control signal by the reactor. The reactor with paralleled a-c windings is much slower than the one with series coils, as a result of the voltage that is induced into the a-c coils by control voltage variations in the d-c winding. In the case of the parallel coils, the induced voltages are additive, and are, of course, in such direction as to oppose the voltage that produced them. When the coils are connected in series, the induced voltages are equal and opposite in the a-c coils, thereby canceling, and producing no time delay.

The response of a reactor is slower when a larger number of turns is used on the control winding, and when the cross section and initial permeability of the core are greater. For large reactors, the response time may be on the order of 10 or more cycles of the excitation frequency. However, the time response of a saturable reactor decreases as the frequency of the a-c source increases. This is fortunate since the use of a higher supply frequency also permits the size of the device to be reduced. Reactors with a-c coils in series are usually used in applications where nominal power is required, and where maximum control speed is required. Reactors with paralleled a-c coils are used in high-power applications where the speed of the reactor response is not of prime concern.

4-7. Magnetic leakage and core construction

When current flows through a coil wound on an iron core, most of the flux produced passes through the core, linking all of the windings. However, although the permeability of the materials used for cores is high, not all of the magnetic field is confined to the core. Some of the flux flows through the air surrounding the core, as shown in Fig. 4-14, or through the insulating material on which the core is wound, so that the two illustrated windings are not linked by the complete flux. This is referred to as magnetic leakage. Furthermore, as core magnetic saturation is approached, the magnetic leakage increases. The leakage must be considered in the design and construction of saturable reactor cores since it reduces the efficiency of the device and increases the time delay in its response. In some cases, the problems caused by the leakage are approached mathematically by assuming the coil to be subdivided into two sections, the main portion producing a flux confined to the core, and the second portion generating the leakage flux. The mathematical results obtained from this basic assumption are excellent approximations to the truth.

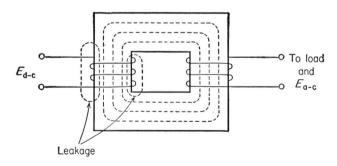

Fig. 4-14. Magnetic leakage in a saturable reactor.

Several practical methods are used to minimize the amount of leakage produced in a reactor. In a single-core device, both coils may be wound on the same limb of the core. Although this construction does reduce the leakage, it necessitates a high degree of insulation between the coils to prevent voltage breakdown and arcing across the adjacent portions of the coils. In a two-core arrangement, the windings are also placed on the same limb of the core to minimize leakage, Fig. 4-15(a), and then the two cores may be overlapped, Fig. 4-15(b), to reduce the space.

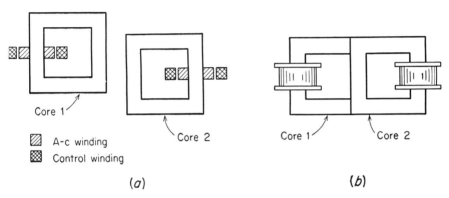

Core 1

▨ A-c winding
▩ Control winding

Core 2   Core 1   Core 2

(a)   (b)

Fig. 4-15. Reducing magnetic leakage in a two-core reactor.

The problem of insulation is not nearly so great in the case of the three-legged core, shown in Fig. 4-16, since there are no closely adjacent windings. Only normal insulation is required in this type of reactor. Unfortunately, however, it has a magnetic leakage greater than that of the split core. This disadvantage may be overcome by using a split core in which the control winding links both cores, as

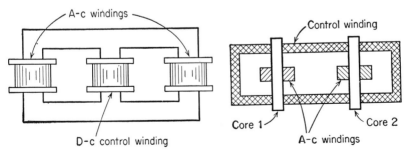

A-c windings

D-c control winding

Control winding

Core 1   Core 2

A-c windings

Fig. 4-16. Three-legged saturable reactor.   Fig. 4-17. Saturable reactor in which
                                              the control winding links two cores.

illustrated in Fig. 4-17. In this reactor, the insulation requirements are held down, and the magnetic leakage is reduced simultaneously.

The four-legged reactor is generally used in applications where it is essential to shield against the stray magnetic fields produced around the reactor. In this reactor, the a-c windings are wound over the center two limbs of the four-legged core, and the d-c winding is placed over the a-c coils. The outer legs of the core act as magnetic shields for the reactor, thereby reducing the stray field to a minimum.

In general, and regardless of whether the reactors under discussion have one, two, three, or four cores, the cores of reactors designed for single-phase applications may be subdivided according to their construction as follows:

    a. Toroids or ring cores
        1. Stacked cores
        2. Spiral cores
    b. Rectangular cores
        1. Stacked cores
        2. Spiral cores

The stacked toroidal core comprises ring-type laminations of core material arranged in a pile to the desired height of the core, as in Fig. 4-18(a). The coil windings are wound toroidally over the core. Figure 4-18(a) illustrates a portion of one winding. The spiral toroidal core construction is used to overcome the difficulties present

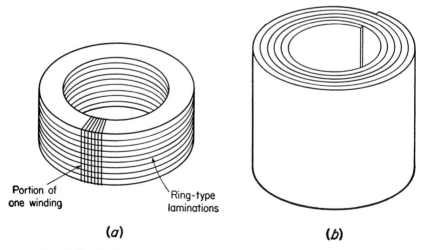

Portion of one winding

Ring-type laminations

(a)

(b)

Fig. 4-18. (a) Construction of a stacked toroidal core. (b) Construction of special toroidal core.

in handling thin laminations. In this core, a strip of core material is wound in the form of a spiral [see Fig. 4-18(b)]. Again the coil windings are applied by using toroidal winding machines. Because of its method of construction, this core is sometimes referred to as a tape-wound core.

The stacked rectangular core consists of rectangular laminations, which may be arranged in UI fashion. To understand the derivation of the "UI" terminology, consider the uncut piece of core material illustrated in Fig. 4-19(a). If a bar of the metal is stamped out along the dotted lines in Fig. 4-19(b), the two UI-shaped pieces of material shown in Fig. 4-19(c) result. If, now, these two pieces are arranged as in Fig. 4-19(d), and are joined along their junction, a rectangular lamination is produced. Rectangular laminations are preferred be-

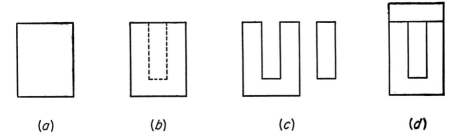

(a)   (b)   (c)   (d)

Fig. 4-19. Procedural steps in the construction of a UI rectangular lamination.

cause they permit the coils to be wound on the straight arbor of a standard high-speed winding machine. In order to maintain a uniform flux density throughout all regions of the core, the rectangular UI laminations are alternated throughout the core. Thus, for the first lamination, the I is placed in a given position [at the top of the U, as in Fig. 4-19(d)]. The next lamination is placed with the I portion in the opposite direction [Fig. 4-19(d) reversed, with the I section on the bottom]. In this manner, the laminations are alternated throughout the height of the core.

The stacked rectangular core may also be constructed in EI fashion, as illustrated in steps (a) through (d), Fig. 4-20. The core material is stamped to produce E and I pieces, which are then joined together to form a three-legged rectangular lamination. These laminations, too, are alternated to produce a constant flux density throughout the core.

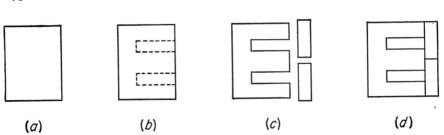

(a) *(b)* *(c)* *(d)*

Fig. 4-20. Procedural steps in the construction of an EI rectangular lamination.

The spiral rectangular core is constructed in much the same manner as the spiral toroidal core, except that the strip of material is wound in rectangular, rather than spiral, form. The spiral configuration is preferred where high, consistent performance of the magnetic amplifier is essential. This is, in part, due to the fact that the tape-wound core can be readily fabricated in very thin gauges of fixed thickness. The stacked core, on the other hand, must be made from carefully punched laminations which cannot be assembled after anneal, for fear of straining the core material.

Three-phase reactors can be produced in any of several ways. The most common method is by placing on top of each other three spiral toroidal cores, each having one load winding. The control winding is wound around the three cores. The result is a three-phase assembly. In another type of construction, three rectangular cores, each with its own load winding, are placed in a Y relationship. The control winding is placed over each of the load windings. Again, the final assembly is a three-phase reactor.

Other reactors with variations of the basic arrangements described in this article may be encountered in the magnetic-amplifier field. In all cases, however, the arrangements are an attempt to obtain a device with a small, inexpensive core, an optimum efficiency consistent with an allowable temperature rise, and low magnetic leakage.

4-8. Multiple control windings

The saturable reactor does not necessarily have but one control winding; in fact, it may have as many as four or six. The control action produced in a reactor with multiple d-c windings is determined by the resultant of the magnetic fields produced by each winding. Thus, the addition of several control windings produces a reactor of great versatility. Control signals from several points in a system may be introduced independently, and remain isolated from each other. The sum of the magnetizing forces produced by the control signals then acts to initiate the required control function.

As an example of the versatility achieved in a device by the use of multiple control windings, consider a reactor with three such windings. One of the windings may be selected to be responsive to a current change in one section of a system; the second winding may be adjusted to be sensitive to a voltage change in another part of the system; and the third may respond to a frequency change in a different portion of the system. The net result is that the reactor can now respond to changes of different types in many different sections of the given system, and thus can provide control action that would be difficult with a different type of circuit.

One control winding of a multiple winding reactor frequently is used to set the state of the core to a convenient operating condition. This winding, the bias winding, is usually fed with d-c produced by rectifying an output of the main a-c supply. Another control winding may be used to inject feedback into the reactor. These will be described in detail in later chapters.

4-9. Current and voltage relationships, forced magnetization

Consider an elementary saturable reactor having one central winding and one load winding. If the windings have an equal number of turns, a change of current in the control winding will produce an effect equivalent to an identical current change in the load winding (assuming no magnetic leakage). Thus, if the current in the d-c winding increases by one ampere, the effect produced will be the same as that obtained by a one-ampere peak swing in the a-c winding. If the control winding turns are increased so that the turns ratio is changed, the same magnetic effect can be produced by a smaller direct current. This is necessarily true since it is the ampere turns of the coil that determine the magnetic flux. In fact, the currents flowing in the control and load windings of a saturable reactor are related by the turns ratio of the windings, similar to their relationship in a current transformer. Hence, if $\mathcal{N}_c$ and $\mathcal{N}_L$ are the control and load windings, respectively, and I_c and I_L are the respective currents, then

$$\mathcal{N}_c I_c = \mathcal{N}_L I_L \qquad (4\text{-}1)$$

This equation may be referred to as the *current transformer equivalency*, and indicates simply that the ampere-turns product of the control windings is equal to that of the load windings. In this relationship, I_L, the a-c load current, is given in terms of average, rather than rms, value.

Note that Eq. (4-1) does not contain any terms relating to supply voltage, supply frequency, or load impedance. Then the saturable reactor can be considered as a controllable constant-current device, which is largely independent of variations in the magnitude, frequency, and waveshape of the a-c source.

The relationship between control and load currents can be derived with reference to the flux produced by the windings. Assume that a sinusoidal voltage is applied to the load coil. The current flowing through the coil sets up a magnetic field proportional to the magnitude of the current and the state of magnetization of the core. If the core is below magnetic saturation, the changing flux causes a counter voltage to be induced into the coil, of amplitude and polarity such as to oppose the voltage that produced it. This results since the applied sinusoidal voltage produces a current lagging by 90 degrees (in a purely inductive circuit), which in turn produces a flux wave lagging the applied voltage by the same 90 degrees. The counter emf generated lags an additional 90 degrees behind the flux, so that a total of 180 degrees exists between the applied and counter voltages.

The shape of the waveforms encountered in a saturable reactor is determined largely by the magnitude of the harmonic currents which flow in the control circuit. The presence or absence of these currents is dependent upon the circuit arrangement. For example, consider the

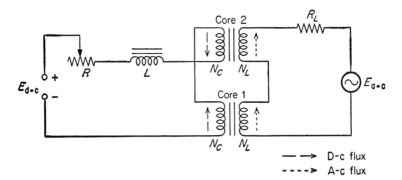

Fig. 4-21. Forced magnetization condition, series-connected a-c winding. *Note:* The flux for only one half of the a-c cycle is illustrated.

circuit of Fig. 4-21, which has series-connected a-c windings and in which a choke is used to limit extraneous currents induced into the control circuit. The presence of the choke causes the control circuit to present a high impedance to the relatively high-magnitude even-harmonic currents, thus tending to suppress them. This sets up a condition referred to as *forced* or *constrained magnetization*, i.e., even-harmonic currents are not permitted to flow freely. The term forced magnetization derives from the fact that the choke prevents the d-c control current from varying, regardless of what happens in the a-c windings, thereby forcing the magnetization to remain at the level determined by the d-c current alone. This condition may also be designated as one of *suppressed even-harmonic currents.*

The dashed arrows of Fig. 4-21 represent the direction of the field produced by the control current; the dotted arrows represent the field produced during one half-cycle of the a-c voltage applied to the load windings. Assume now that the control current is sufficient to move both cores into positive saturation. During the half-cycle illustrated in Fig. 4-21, the a-c current flowing in the load coil of core 1 (which lags the voltage by up to 90 degrees) can produce no change in magnetization, since the core is presently saturated. Because the flux cannot change, no voltage can develop across this winding, which acts as if it were short-circuited. The flat-topped magnetization state, which is shown in Fig. 4-22, and which indicates core saturation, exists for core 1.

During this same half-cycle, the load current produces a field of direction opposite to that produced by the control current in core 2. The a-c field is such as to bring core 2 out of its positive saturated state, and move it over the linear section of the *B-H* curve toward negative saturation (saturation in the reverse direction). Thus the core 2 magnetization state varies during this half-cycle as illustrated in Fig. 4-22. The change in flux generates a counter voltage across the a-c coil of core 2.

On the next half-cycle, similar circuit conditions exist. However, core 2 now is saturated while the state of core 1 varies sinusoidally. As a result of these conditions, the load current has a nearly rectangular waveform, as seen in Fig. 4-22. This indicates that the third harmonic and other odd harmonics are of such phase as to produce the flat-topped current waveform. The magnitude of this current is dependent upon the control current and the turns ratio of the circuit, but is substantially independent of the magnitude of the applied a-c voltage.

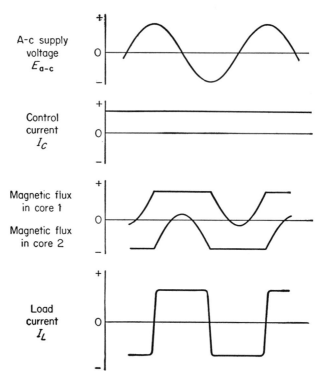

Fig. 4-22. Waveforms existing under forced magnetization conditions.

Before proceeding to natural magnetization, it must be noted that a high control-circuit impedance will necessarily produce the forced magnetization condition in any reactor which has one control winding and one load winding. However, in this case of multiple control windings, each and every control winding must be of high impedance for this condition to result.

Forced magnetization is frequently used in conjunction with non-feedback circuits for measuring large direct currents and in oscillographic investigations.

4-10. Natural magnetization

In a saturable-reactor circuit with series-connected a-c windings and a low impedance control circuit (no series choke), even harmonic currents are not damped out, but rather flow freely in the control network. This represents the condition of *natural magnetization*, and is the condition under which most reactors operate. The current and voltage waveforms obtained under this condition are shown in Fig. 4-23. Note that the d-c control current, in the absence of the series choke, is not held at a fixed value but rather is a pulsating d-c, varying above and below its mean value. This results from the double-frequency component currents induced into the control winding by the changing flux in the core not at saturation. In order for the load current to maintain the required sinusoidal change in flux, it must take on the sharp-pulsed appearance of Fig. 4-23. The mean value of this current, as well as that in the control winding, is not altered; the $N_C I_C = N_L I_L$ relationship still exists.

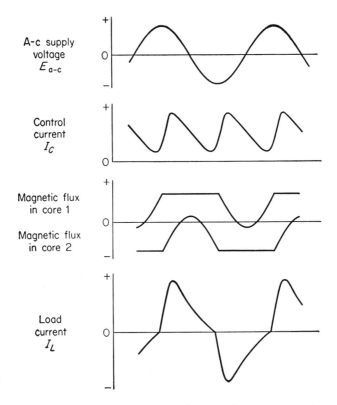

Fig. 4-23. Natural magnetization, voltage and current waveforms.

The waveforms shown in Fig. 4-23 are derived from an idealized *B-H* curve, in which core saturation is reached suddenly and completely. Practical waveforms are illustrated in Fig. 4-24; note that the shapes vary depending upon the permeability of the core.

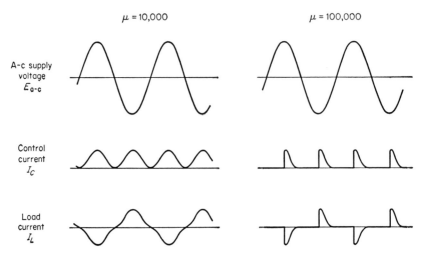

Fig. 4-24. Current and voltage waveforms for cores of different permeability.

4-11. Load limitation

In any practical circuit, the a-c windings of the saturable reactor are connected in series with a load. The load resistance, plus the resistance of the windings, are a limiting factor so far as the load current is concerned. Theoretically, if the load resistance were zero, the current peaks would reach infinity.

The load resistance has little effect on the current waveform, and for normal values of resistance, will not change the waveform to any great degree. If the resistance is excessively large, the load current peaks are limited in amplitude, and the transformer current equivalency does not hold true; that is, $N_L I_L$ will be less than $N_c I_c$. With large loads, practically all of the applied voltage appears across the load resistance, and the load current (E applied$/R$) is reduced to a value too small to be effective. Under this condition, the d-c winding loses its control. (See Art. 6-3.)

4-12. Parallel-connected a-c windings

Consider now the saturable reactor in which the a-c windings are connected in parallel, operating under natural magnetization conditions, Fig. 4-25. For the half-cycle illustrated, core 1 is at saturation, so that there can be no change in flux in this core, and no voltage developed across core 1 load coil. In addition, since the a-c coils are connected in parallel, no voltage can appear across the core 2 a-c coil. Hence, these windings are shorted out in this half-cycle, and all of the

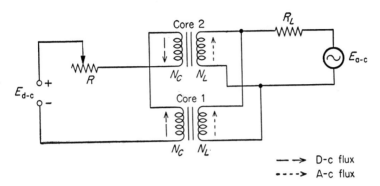

Fig. 4-25. Parallel-connected saturable reactor. *Note:* The flux for only one half of the a-c cycle is shown.

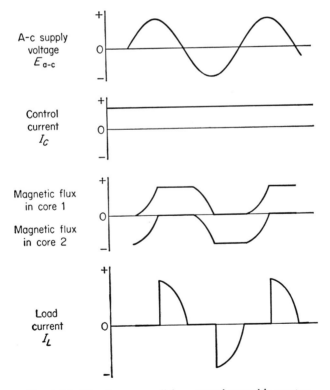

Fig. 4-26. Waveforms, parallel-connected saturable reactor.

applied voltage appears across the load resistance. The load current is then determined by the applied voltage and the load resistance.

This action may be seen in Fig. 4-26. On the initial half-cycle, the core 1 magnetization rises to saturation. When this occurs, the flux can no longer change and, as pointed out before, no voltage is developed across either load winding. Thus the state of magnetization in core 2 necessarily is held constant at the value it has reached. A current pulse equal to E applied$/R$ is developed at this point. When the applied voltage reverses direction, core 1 magnetization decreases below saturation, while core 2 rises to saturation. At core 2 saturation, both fluxes reach a fixed value, and a second current pulse is produced.

Although the amplitude of current pulse is determined primarily by the load resistance and the applied voltage, nevertheless the current transformer equivalency holds true provided that the resistance is not excessively large. The pulse actually delays the applicable core in its approach to saturation, so that it does not saturate until somewhat later in the cycle. At this time, the applied voltage has decreased in value, and the pulse produced is of smaller amplitude and of decreased duration.

Two points should be noted with reference to the parallel connection. In the first place, no voltage is induced from the load windings into the control windings. Since the load current flows in the a-c windings during the period when both cores are magnetically saturated, there are no flux changes to induce pulsating currents into the control coil. Secondly, the fact that the a-c windings are short-circuited over a considerable portion of the cycle introduces a time delay in the control-circuit response.

4-13. Control response and time constant

In general, the control voltage applied to the control windings of the reactor is a varying, rather than a steady, signal. This signal may be of sinusoidal or any other form, and will be applied to the reactor in addition to any steady voltage produced by bias or feedback. In most cases (except with respect to transients), it is noted that variations in amplitude of the control current will appear in the output spread over several cycles of the a-c supply frequency. As a result, the current-equivalency relationship holds true.

The time constant t of a reactor refers to the time required for the reactor output current to reach 63 per cent of its new value when a step voltage is applied to the control windings. Since the saturable reactor is a highly inductive device, the control flux cannot rise instantaneously, but will build up exponentially at a rate depending on the constants of the input circuit. Thus, in Fig. 4-27, when the step voltage occurs in the control circuit, the output current rises from its original value of I at time t_1 to its final value of I_3 at time t_3. If value I_2 represents 63 per cent of final current I_3, then the time difference between t_1 and t_2 is the time constant of the reactor.

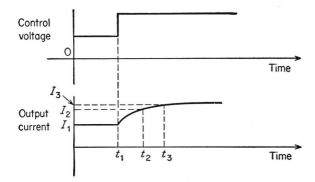

Fig. 4-27. Delay in response of output current to step voltage in control circuit.

The time constant of the circuit is given by

$$t = \frac{L}{R} \text{ seconds} \tag{4-2}$$

where t = time constant in seconds
L = inductance of the control winding in henries
R = resistance of the control winding circuit in ohms.

It follows that the greater the number of turns in the control winding, and the greater the cross section and initial permeability of the core, the greater will be the inductance of the reactor, and the slower will be its response. In large reactors, the response time may be 10 or more cycles of the supply frequency.

To increase the speed of response of the reactor, e.g., to decrease the time constant, an external resistor, called a forcing resistor, is often placed in series with the control winding. As can be seen from Eq. (4-2), an increase in R will lead to a decrease in t. However, a disadvantage of increasing the speed of response by this method is that a portion of the control signal power is dissipated across the forcing resistor.

In conclusion, it should be noted that experimentation is presently being carried on with magnetic amplifiers having non-inductive control windings. It is hoped thereby to obtain an almost instantaneous response in the load circuit to variations in the control circuit.

REVIEW QUESTIONS

1. When the control voltage is 1.5 v in the circuit of Fig. 4-6(a), the inductance of the load winding is 500 millihenries. If the load resistance is 500 ohms, and the a-c supply voltage is 110 v at 60 cycles, what is the voltage across the load resistance? (Neglect load winding resistance.)

2. Differentiate between the terms *natural magnetization* and *forced magnetization*. In which case are even-harmonic currents damped out?

3. The inductance of a control winding of a saturable reactor is 4 henries. (a) If the resistance of the winding is 50 ohms, what is the time constant of the circuit? (b) What value forcing resistor will decrease the time constant to 0.01 sec?

CHAPTER

5

Applications of Saturable Reactors

5-1. Introduction

The basic saturable reactor has been in use for many years in control, measurement, regulation, and positioning circuits and equipments, primarily as an a-c control device. The fundamental reactor circuit is used as a single unit and not in cascade. The power gain obtained with the single device is low, usually 10 or less. Only a few of the more common and useful applications of the devices will be described in this chapter. It must be emphasized that the circuits included in the following pages are representative examples of the uses devised for saturable reactor devices.

The control characteristic of the fundamental saturable reactor consists of two equally sloped portions, as shown in Fig. 5-1. Thus, in the basic circuit, polarity-sensitive operation is not feasible.

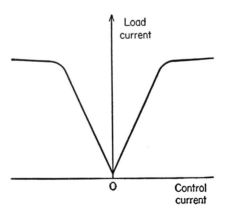

Fig. 5-1. Control characteristics of a saturable reactor.

5-2. Theatre-light control using saturable reactors

The saturable reactor has been adapted to the control of the lighting systems in modern theatres. In each of the systems, control must be maintained over several hundred light groups. In the absence of saturable reactors, each group might require control by rheostats or potentiometers. At the voltages encountered, this would be most inefficient because of the heat losses dissipated across the variable resistances; furthermore, the control would be difficult because of the manual efforts involved in moving the contacts of these large resistances. With the advent of the saturable reactor and its application to this type of control, the basic problem was solved. Each light group in the theatre is controlled by a small lever, mounted on a panel; the lever, in turn, controls the impedance of a saturable reactor, thus affecting the brightness or dimness of the light group in question. All the levers controlling the hundreds of light groups are located on a master control panel. Small switches permit large numbers of levers to be joined together, so that one lever can then be used to control scores of light groups.

Figure 5-2 illustrates the basic saturable-reactor circuit used to control one of the theatre light groups. A-c line voltage is applied to the circuit through transformer T_1. The line voltage is boosted to compensate for the voltage drop across the saturable reactor when it is fully saturated. If this drop were 10 volts, and the line voltage 110 volts, then the total voltage that could be applied to the lamps, in the absence of compensation, would be 100 volts. If conventional 110-volt bulbs were used, they would never be lighted to their full brilliance. By using the transformer, the applied voltage may be increased to 120 volts. A 10-volt drop across the reactor reduces the lamp voltage to 110 volts, the lamp's rated value. Thus, compensation is complete.

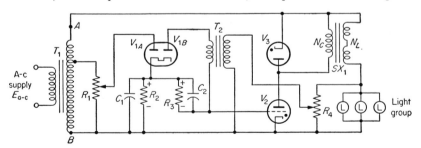

Fig. 5-2. Controlling a theatre light group by means of a saturable-reactor circuit. (*After General Electric Company.*)

The a-c load winding N_L of the saturable reactor SX_1 is connected in series with the load (which is the light group, in this application). The division of a-c voltage between N_L and the load is determined, of course, by the impedance of N_L, which in turn is controlled by the d-c current flowing in the control winding N_C of the reactor. This current is supplied from thyratron V_2 and gaseous diode (phanotron) V_3. On the positive half-cycle, i.e., when the V_2 plate voltage is positive, direct plate current flows through N_C, and magnetic flux is set up. On the negative half-cycle, no V_2 current flows, and the flux around N_C starts to collapse. The self-induced voltage generated by the collapsing field is of such polarity as to drive the cathode of V_3 negative, and its plate positive. As a result, V_3 conducts, forcing direct current through N_C in the same direction as the previous current. Thus, current flows through the control winding in the same direction over the complete cycle.

The actual magnitude of control current (this is of prime importance, since it determines the impedance of the reactor) is controlled by the grid bias on the thyratron. This potential determines the instant in the half-cycle at which the thyratron starts to conduct. On the half-cycle when point A is positive with respect to point B, half-wave rectifier V_{1A} conducts, producing a voltage of indicated polarity across resistor R_2. Capacitor C_1 charges to the same polarity. On the next half-cycle, the load voltage appearing across potentiometer R_4 (R_4 is in parallel with the load) causes a voltage to be induced into the secondary of T_2, of such polarity as to drive the plate of V_{1B} positive. This tube section conducts, and develops a voltage of indicated polarity across R_3. Capacitor C_2 charges to the same polarity.

Note that the grid-to-cathode potential of thyratron V_2 is the resultant of the opposing d-c voltages across resistors R_2 and R_3. The voltage across R_2 acts as to drive the grid of the thyratron in a positive direction and is therefore referred to as the turn-on voltage. The voltage across R_3 drives the grid negative, and is referred to as the turn-off voltage.

To follow the over-all operation of this circuit, assume that the arm of potentiometer R_1 is at the uppermost position. Full line voltage is rectified by V_{1A} and the turn-on voltage across R_2 is at its maximum. Thus, the thyratron conducts with top ability, and maximum control current flows through the control winding of the reactor. The reactor impedance is now at minimum value, and the voltage across the load at maximum. The lights are bright. When the arm of potentiometer R_1 is moved downward, the voltage across R_2 decreases. As a result, the grid-to-bias potential of V_2 moves in a negative direction, and thyratron V_2 plate current decreases. The resultant increase in impedance of the reactor causes the load voltage to be reduced, and the lights are dimmed.

Potentiometer R_4 is added to the circuit to give it increased control range. When the arm of this potentiometer is in its uppermost position, the voltage applied to rectifier V_{1B}, and therefore the turn-off developed across R_3, is at its maximum. This determines the maximum brightness level, which may be reduced by varying potentiometer R_2. Although the illustrated circuit indicates only two variable resistances, the light group voltage may be controlled by more elaborate means to permit fading and other effects required during a theatrical production.

A final point to be made is that in this unit the saturable reactor acts essentially as a constant-voltage device; thus it holds the light group brightness at a relatively fixed level even if a lamp in the group should burn out or be removed from the circuit. If, for example, a lamp does burn out, the current flowing through the a-c winding of the reactor decreases, the drop across the a-c winding decreases, and the load voltage increases, causing the light group brilliance to increase. However, the increase in load voltage is paralleled by the increase across the primary of T_2. The increased T_2 secondary voltage leads to a rise in the E_{R3} turn-off voltage, so that thyratron plate current diminishes. This leads to an increase in reactor impedance, causing the a-c winding voltage to increase, thereby bringing the light group voltage back to its original value.

5-3. Electric furnace control

A circuit similar to that used for theatre-light control is shown in Fig. 5-3. The purpose of this circuit is to maintain accurate control over an industrial electric furnace, so that the temperature of the furnace will be held constant. This is important in applications such as galvanizing and sintering where a small temperature fluctuation may lead to deterioration of the product quality. The power under control may be as high as 1000 kva.

Figure 5-3 represents a simplified version of the heating control circuit. Resistance R_1 is a slide-wire potentiometer controlled by a

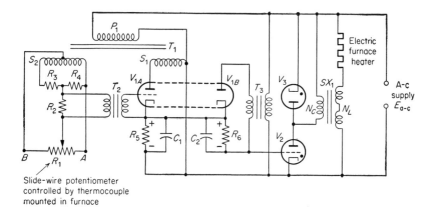

Slide-wire potentiometer
controlled by thermocouple
mounted in furnace

Fig. 5-3. Saturable-reactor control of an electric furnace. (*After General Electric Company.*)

thermocouple mounted in the furnace. Note that the a-c supply voltage is applied to the primary P_1 of transformer T_1, so that a voltage is induced into the two secondaries, S_1 and S_2, of the transformer. Assume that the electric heaters of the furnace are causing an increase in furnace temperature. The thermocouple control element in the furnace causes the arm of potentiometer R_1 to move toward point A. The resistance between the arm of R_1 and the right end of the potentiometer decreases, while R_2, of course, remains fixed. Thus, the a-c voltage developed across R_2 increases. (The voltage across R_4 may be considered as a source applied to the series circuit comprising R_2 and the right portion of R_1. When this latter resistance decreases, the voltage across R_2 increases.) The increasing voltage across R_2 is applied to the primary of T_2, inducing an increased voltage into the grid circuit of V_{1A}. This voltage reduces the plate current of V_{1A} during the half-cycle when the V_{1A} anode voltage is positive, thereby decreasing the turn-on potential developed across R_5. As a result, thyratron V_2 (and subsequently phanotron V_3) supply a reduced control current to the saturable reactor. The impedance of the reactor increases, lowering the voltage applied to the load, and the furnace temperature decreases in an attempt to offset the increase that led to this chain of events.

When the thermocouple records a decreasing temperature, it moves the arm of the slide-wire potentiometer toward point B, initiating control action to raise the heater voltage and furnace temperature.

5-4. Battery charging control

The saturable reactor can be applied to the control of a battery charging circuit, as shown in Fig. 5-4. The illustrated circuit is used to charge a large 125- or 144-volt storage battery, maintaining it at close

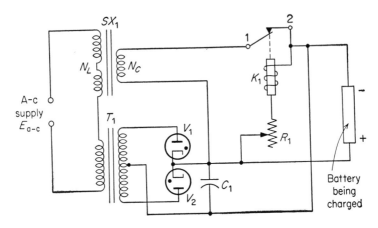

Fig. 5-4. Saturable-reactor control of a battery-charging circuit.

to its full charge as long as the circuit is operative. In this manner, the life of the battery is increased. The a-c supply voltage is applied to the series combination of the reactor load windings and the primary of transformer T_1. The secondary voltage is rectified by full-wave gaseous rectifiers V_1 and V_2, and the d-c output voltage appears across relay coil K_1 and rheostat R_1, which are in parallel with the d-c winding of the saturable reactor in one branch, and with the battery under charge in another.

When the voltage across this parallel network is relatively low, as it will be when the battery is being charged, the potential will not be sufficiently large to actuate the relay. The direct control current flowing through the normally closed contacts of the relay will saturate the reactor, so that most of the applied a-c voltage appears across the transformer. The large voltage applied to the rectifiers acts to maintain their output at a high level, so that the battery will charge.

When the battery becomes charged to its normal high level, the voltage across the relay coil increases, and the relay is actuated. The open relay contacts interrupt the circuit to the d-c control winding, so that the reactor now assumes a high impedance. As a result, the voltage applied to the transformer decreases, and the rectified output decreases. As soon as the battery voltage diminishes sufficiently (as power is dissipated by the load), the relay contacts close, and the cycle repeats. The setting of the rheostat determines the level of battery voltage to be maintained. When the rheostat is set so that it inserts low resistance in the circuit, the voltage level is low.

5-5. Phase-shifting applications

One of the most common and useful applications of the saturable reactor is in the phase control of a thyratron grid voltage. It will be recalled that prior to its conduction, a thyratron acts as an open circuit. Once the gas contained in the tube ionizes, and the tube conducts, the tube closely resembles a short circuit; it will continue to conduct as long as the anode is slightly positive. Thyratron control is tied to the control of its grid in the interval preceding tube conduction; simply choosing the point during the cycle when the grid will permit the tube to conduct will determine the output of the thyratron. If the grid voltage is of proper phase and direction so as to allow the thyratron to fire early in the cycle, the thyratron output will be high. If, however, the thyratron conduction is delayed until late in the cycle, its output will be low. By this means of thyratron control, the outputs of rectifiers can be varied, motor speeds can be changed over wide ranges, and numerous other electronic processes can be controlled.

A saturable reactor used for grid-voltage phase control is illustrated in Fig. 5-5(a). The a-c winding N_L of the reactor is part of an R-L

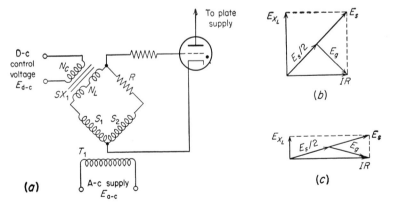

Fig. 5-5. (a) Use of a saturable reactor for thyratron grid control. (b) Vector relationship in absence of control current. (c) Vector relationship in presence of control current.

bridge network, the other arms being a fixed resistor R and the center-tapped secondary winding of a transformer T_1. A-c voltage $E_{a\text{-}c}$ is applied to the primary of the transformer, and a d-c control voltage $E_{d\text{-}c}$ is applied to the control winding of SX_1.

Assume that initially no control current flows in the N_C winding of the reactor, so that the impedance of the reactor is at its maximum. If this maximum is 10,000 ohms, and if R_1 has been selected to be 10,000 ohms, the vector relationship of Fig. 5-5(b) is derived. From this it may be noted that the secondary voltage E_s may be divided into two components, one resistive and one inductive. The voltage IR developed across the resistor is 90 degrees out of phase with respect to the voltage E_{XL} developed across the a-c winding of the reactor. Further, the grid voltage E_g (the voltage between grid and cathode of the thyratron), which is the vector resultant of IR and $E_s/2$, lags the secondary voltage by 90 degrees. Since in this circuit the anode supply is the same a-c source, the grid voltage lags the anode voltage by 90 degrees, and the tube fires late in the half-cycle. As a result, a relatively low average thyratron plate current flows.

When d-c control voltage is applied to the saturable reactor, the impedance of the reactor diminishes, possibly to 2,500 ohms. The new vector relationship is given in Fig. 5-5(c). Under these conditions, the grid voltage lags the anode voltage by considerably less than 90 degrees — actually it approaches a zero degree phase angle as the control current increases — and the tube fires earlier in the half-cycle. The result is that a relatively large average thyratron plate current flows.

Thus, by this phase-shifting method, a small range of reactor current can be used to vary thyratron plate current between wide limits. If this plate current is used to control an action, such as changing a motor speed, the speed variation can be controlled with accuracy over a wide range of speeds.

5-6. Saturable-reactor circuits for d-c and oscillographic measurements

The simple saturable-reactor circuit can be modified for application to the direct measurement of large direct currents, between 100 and 50,000 amperes, that flow in a d-c bus in a high-power installation. The circuit of the device, illustrated in Fig. 5-6(a), uses a twin-core saturable reactor to measure the direct bus current. In this circuit, the a-c load windings of the saturable reactor are connected in series opposing; the d-c bus itself, placed within the twin cores, acts as the d-c control winding of the reactor.

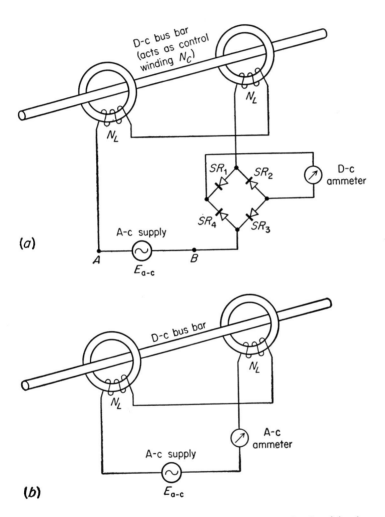

Fig. 5-6. D-c measurement using a saturable-reactor circuit: (a) using d-c ammeter; (b) using a-c ammeter.

The a-c supply voltage is applied to the reactor load windings. The current I_L flowing through these windings is determined by their impedance.* The load current flowing through the ammeter — an iron-vane ammeter calibrated in d-c units is generally used — is unidirectional, since the bridged rectifiers will permit a current flow in but one direction. Thus if point A of the a-c source is negative, electrons will flow through the load windings, through SR_2, then through the ammeter and SR_4 back to the source. On the next half-cycle, electrons flow through SR_3, through the ammeter in the same direction as during the previous half-cycle, then through SR_1 and the load windings back to the source.

The magnitude of the direct current I_C in the bus determines the magnetic flux around the conductor, and thus sets the level of magnetization in the reactor cores. This flux, in turn, controls the impedance of the load windings, thus directly affecting the amplitude of the load circuit I_L. If then the direct bus current increases, the impedance of the load windings decreases, the load current increases, and the ammeter indicates a higher value of direct current. This circuit operation is based directly upon the current-transformer characteristics of the reactor, described earlier in Chapter 4, and the saturable reactor in this application frequently is referred to as a direct-current transformer.

One advantage of the saturable-reactor circuit for d-c measurement is that no meter shunt resistors are required. The resistors needed for the measurement of thousands of amperes are large, costly, and difficult to cool. In addition, the reactor method of measurement isolates the metering circuit from the d-c bus, which assumes importance when the bus is at a high potential with respect to ground. Furthermore, variations in currents in the bus produce instantaneous indications on the meter.

Figure 5-6(b) differs from 5-6(a) in that no rectifiers are present, so that an a-c ammeter is used for the current measurement. Other than this, the circuit operation is the same as described for (a).

A saturable-reactor circuit similar to those described can be used to make oscillographic measurements. In this circuit (not shown) a single-core (rather than twin-core) reactor is used, through which a

---

* The actual impedance of the windings varies over the half-cycle of the applied voltage; it is large during the first portion of the half-cycle, but decreases to a small value during the remainder of the time. Because of the periodic insertion and removal of this large impedance, the operation of the reactor is sometimes considered analogous to that of a switch, which is open during the first portion of the half-cycle, and closed during the latter portion.

d-c bus bar is placed. Again, the bus acts as the control winding of the saturable reactor. The a-c supply voltage is applied to a series circuit comprising the load winding N_L and an oscillographic shunt resistor R. The alternating current on the bus is induced from primary (bus) to secondary (load winding) in the manner of a conventional current transformer, and the a-c voltage developed across the shunt resistor is applied to the oscillograph. When the bus current contains a pulsating d-c component, the state of core magnetization increases and the load current I_L will increase. However, the effect of this increased current will not radically change the oscillographic voltage picked off the shunt resistor R, and the oscillographic picture produced remains quite accurate.

5-7. Polarity-sensitive saturable reactors

It was indicated earlier in this chapter, with reference to the control characteristic of the saturable reactor shown in Fig. 5-1, that the reactor was not polarity-sensitive. The output obtained with either negative or positive values of control current does not change sign or amplitude. One method of providing discrimination between negative and positive signals is illustrated in Fig. 5-7(a). Two rectifiers, SR_1 and SR_2, are connected in series with the a-c windings N_{L1} and N_{L2} of saturable reactor SX_1. When the a-c supply has the circled polarity, load current flows through winding N_{L1}, rectifier SR_1, and resistor R_1 in such direction as to produce a voltage of indicated polarity across R_1. On the next half-cycle, current flows through N_{L2}, SR_2, and R_2 to develop the indicated voltage drop across R_2. Thus, the presence of the rectifiers permits only a unidirectional current to flow through the reactor load windings.

In the absence of direct control current, the impedance of the reactor is at its maximum. As a result, the output voltage (on one half-cycle across R_1, and on the next half-cycle across R_2 is at its minimum. This is shown in the curve of Fig. 5-7(b).

Control current in the d-c winding of the saturable reactor can flow, of course, in either of two directions. In one case, the magnetic flux produced by the control current can be in the same direction as the flux produced by the unidirectional load current in the load windings. Under these conditions, the control current is said to be flowing in the positive or forward direction, and the core rapidly approaches magnetic saturation. As a result, the impedance of the re-

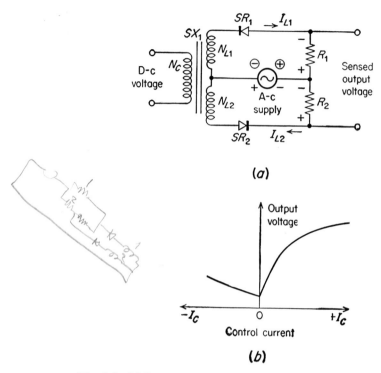

Fig. 5-7. (a) Rectifier-polarized saturable reactor. (*After A. L. Whitley and L. C. Ludbrook, United States patent 2,229,952.*) (b) Output voltage plotted against control current.

actor decreases, and the output voltage increases. [Refer to Fig. 5-7(b).]

In summary, then, this magnetic amplifier is polarity-sensitive, and will produce two different outputs, as determined by a forward (positive) or reverse (negative) control current.

Figure 5-8(a) illustrates the manner in which a truly polarity-sensitive magnetic amplifier can be connected. In this circuit as shown, the rectifiers are wired such that load current can flow through windings N_{L1} and N_{L2} only on the same half-cycle (namely when the a-c supply has the circled polarity). Load current I_{L2} flows through R_2 and through N_{L2}. Load current I_{L1} flows through R_1 and through N_{L1}. Thus, the magnetic flux produced around N_{L1} is in the opposite direction to that of N_{L2}. In the absence of control current, the output voltage taken across R_1 and R_2 is zero, as shown in Fig. 5-8(b).

When control current of one specified direction is applied to N_c, the flux set up around this winding will aid the flux produced around one load winding and oppose that produced around the other load winding. For example, if the control current is of such direction that the N_C flux aids the N_{L1} flux, it must of necessity oppose the N_{L2} flux. Thus the impedance of the N_{L1} winding is decreased, and the voltage across R_1 increased, while the impedance of N_{L2} winding is increased,

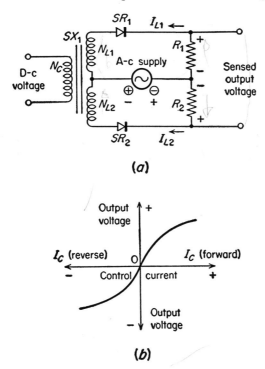

Fig. 5-8. (a) A second polar ity-sensitive saturable reactor. (b) Output voltage plotted against control current.

and the voltage across R_2 decreased. As a result, with the control current direction as specified, the sensed output voltage is negative [see Fig. 5-8(b)]. Thus the control current can be referred to as being in a forward direction. When the control current direction is reversed, or in the negative direction, the sensed output is a negative voltage [Fig. 5-8(b)].

The saturable-reactor circuits described in this article have a high efficiency with respect to power-handling capacity. Furthermore, rectifier-polarized amplifiers may be placed in cascade with little difficulty since the amplifier output is zero when the control current input is zero.

5-8. Resonant control circuits

The principles of series and parallel resonance are sometimes applied to saturable-reactor circuits to extend the range of control. As an example, note that capacitors C_1 and C_2 have been added to the basic reactor circuit illustrated in Fig. 5-9 to produce resonant conditions. Capacitor C_1 forms a series resonant circuit with the load winding of the reactor, and capacitor C_2 forms a parallel resonant circuit with it.

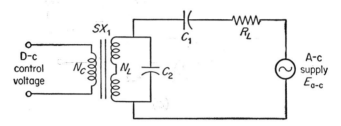

Fig. 5-9. Use of series and parallel resonance to extend the range of control of a saturable reactor.

To understand how the control range is extended, it will be recalled that, in the absence of a series capacitor, increasing the direct control current causes the impedance of the load winding to decrease, thereby permitting the load current to increase. When the control current rises beyond a certain value, the reactor core becomes saturated magnetically, and the load current levels off at a fixed value. The magnitude of the load current is determined by the inductive reactance displayed by the load winding at saturation. The X_L will be low, but not zero.

In the presence of a series capacitor, selected judiciously to form a resonant circuit with the load winding, the reactances of the capacitor and the inductor effectively cancel each other. Thus, theoretically at least, the opposition offered by the series circuit at resonance is zero; practically, of course, the opposition approaches, but does not reach, zero. As a result, much larger values of load current flow now than in the absence of the series capacitor. Consequently, the addition of the capacitor increases the range of control of the reactor.

Capacitor C_2 is selected to form a parallel resonant circuit with the load winding. If the capacitor is not considered, the maximum inductive reactance — and this will be a finite value — occurs when the control current is at its minimum. Considering the resonant circuit formed by the capacitor and the load winding, it will be remembered that the impedance of a parallel circuit at resonance theoretically is infinite, and practically may be very large. As a result, in the absence of control current, but in the presence of the parallel resonant circuit, the load current is decreased to an exceedingly small value. Again, the range of control of the saturable reactor is increased.

CHAPTER

6

The Magnetic Amplifier
without Feedback

6-1. Introduction

Generally the single-stage and multistage magnetic amplifiers used in commercial and industrial applications make use of a positive internal (intrinsic) or external (extrinsic) feedback, thus increasing the power amplification of the devices. These circuits are, however, based on the characteristics of the fundamental magnetic amplifiers which have no such feedback. Because of this, it is necessary first to discuss the low-gain devices that do not use feedback, as a stepping stone to the future discussion of feedback magnetic amplifiers. In addition, it must be noted that although feedback magnetic amplifiers have many applications, this does not imply necessarily that the elementary magnetic amplifiers are without value. Despite their lack of power gain, these devices do have certain useful applications, which will be described in this and later chapters.

As mentioned in Chapter 4, the magnetic amplifier consists of combinations of saturable reactors, rectifiers, resistors, and transformers. Its advantages, outlined toward the conclusion of this chapter, permit the magnetic amplifier to be applied successfully in a wide variety of uses. Whereas the saturable reactor is primarily important as an a-c control device, the magnetic amplifier may be applied to systems concerned with temperature (heat) control, motor speed control, voltage and frequency regulation, magnetic modulation, audio and servo amplification, etc. A major difference between the saturable reactor and the magnetic amplifier lies in their method of control. While the saturable-reactor device is normally controlled by a single signal, the magnetic amplifier frequently has multiple control windings, so that the amplifier is controlled by the resultant effect of all the windings.

6-2. Basic magnetic-amplifier circuit

An elementary, but practical, magnetic-amplifier circuit is illustrated in Fig. 6-1(a). In this circuit, saturable reactor SX_1 is used in conjunction with dry-disc rectifier SR_1 to produce a controllable d-c

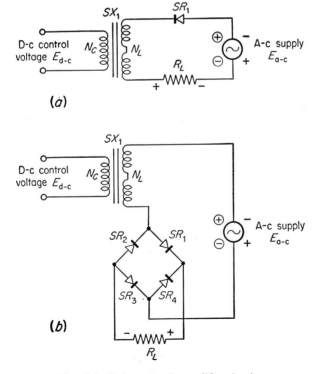

Fig. 6-1. Basic magnetic-amplifier circuits.

voltage across the load resistance R_L. The magnitude of the R_L voltage is determined by the magnitude of the d-c control voltage E_{d-c}. No feedback is used in this circuit. Assume that no control voltage is applied to control winding N_C, and that the circuit is being examined on the half-cycle when the a-c supply has the circled polarity. At this time, electrons flow from the negative potential point of the a-c supply through load resistance R_L, series-opposing load windings N_L, and rectifier SR_1 to the positive terminal of the supply. On the next half-cycle, no conduction occurs because of the rectifier connection. Thus, a half-wave rectified d-c voltage appears across the load resistance.

As was stated, the magnitude of the load voltage is determined by the d-c control voltage. When no voltage is applied to the control winding N_C, this winding contributes no flux to the reactor core, so that the total flux is produced by the load windings. As a result, the N_L impedance is at its maximum. Thus, the portion of the a-c supply voltage appearing across the N_L windings is high, and that across the rectifiers is low. The rectified voltage is at a minimum.

When d-c control voltage of either polarity is supplied to the N_C winding, the impedance of the load windings decreases, with a consequent rise in the R_L output voltage. Because small control currents produce large changes in load current, and consequently in load power, a substantial gain can be realized from this circuit. The rectification is required so that the a-c flowing in the load circuit is changed to the same form as the d-c in the control circuit. This permits the current transformer equivalency, Eq. (4-1), to become effective.

The basic circuit of Fig. 6-1(a) may be referred to as either a *nonpolarized magnetic amplifier* or a *polarized magnetic amplifier*, depending only upon the connection of the load windings. If the load windings are connected in series opposition, as they are normally, a nonpolarized condition arises, and the amplifier cannot discriminate between control currents of opposite polarities. This derives from the fact that, with control current of any given polarity flowing in the control winding, the flux produced by this winding will at all times aid the flux produced by one of the load windings while opposing the flux produced by the other. As a result, the direction of the control current has no effect upon the load voltage; the magnitude of the current is the important factor.

If the load windings of the reactor of Fig. 6-1(a) are connected in series aiding, a polarized magnetic amplifier results. Since the flux produced by the load windings will always be in the same direction, the flux around the control windings will either aid or oppose the load winding flux as determined by the direction of control current. This means that the amplifier can distinguish between control signal polarities.

Figure 6-1(b) illustrates a full-wave magnetic amplifier which operates in similar fashion to the circuit in (a). In this circuit, however, load current flows on both half-cycles of the a-c supply, through rectifiers SR_1 and SR_3 when the supply has the circled polarity, and through rectifiers SR_2 and SR_4 on the next half-cycle. A full-wave rectified controllable voltage appears across R_L in this variation of the basic magnetic amplifier.

6-3. Load lines

The selection of the load resistance in a non-feedback magnetic-amplifier circuit is important in that an incorrect value can affect the current equivalency relationship of the reactor, expressed in Eq. (4-1). The equivalency is valid only over the linear portion of the characteristic curve; thus if the value of load resistance is excessively high, the load current is too small and the equivalency cannot be satisfied.

To understand the selection and use of load lines, note the family of static characteristic curves illustrated in Fig. 6-2, in which load current I_L is plotted against load winding voltage E_{NL} for different values of control current I_C. The particular load line shown has a slope corresponding to $0G/0A$, equivalent to a load resistance of approximately 600 ohms. (All values specified in this discussion are taken with reference to average values of current and voltage. If the graph were plotted in dissimilar units, as with I_L in average value and E_{NL} in rms units, then a conversion would be necessary prior to any description.)

Under conditions of $I_C = 0$ ma, the operating point of the magnetic amplifier will be at F on the load line. This corresponds to a load current of about 6 milliamperes and a load voltage of about 96 volts. In the selection of the load line, satisfactory operation will not occur if the point F intersection is taken too close to the upward bend in the $I_C = 0$ ma characteristic; when operating near the bend, small variations in the applied voltage can lead to excessively large variations in load current.

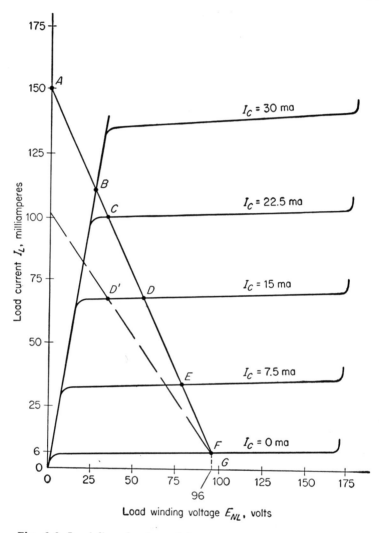

Fig. 6-2. Load lines for determining operating limits of a magnetic amplifier.

When the control current I_C is increased (to 7.5, 15, and 22.5 ma in Fig. 6-2), the load current I_L also increases. However, the actual voltage across the a-c windings of the reactor will evidently decrease because of the increased voltage drop $I_L R_L$. Thus for $I_C = 7.5$ ma, $I_L = 35$ ma and $E_{NL} = 85$ v; for $I_C = 15$ ma, $I_L = 70$ ma and $E_{NL} = 65$ v; and for $I_C = 22.5$ ma, $I_L = 102$ ma and $E_{NL} = 35$ v. For each value of control current, the actual operating point of the device is given by the intersection of the load line with the applicable curve, at points E, D, and C.

The maximum useful control current as shown in Fig. 6-2 is a little more than 22.5 milliamperes. This is evident since the load line intersects the horizontal portion of the $I_C = 22.5$ ma curve, but does not cross the horizontal portion of the $I_C = 30$ ma curve. If the control current exceeds the useful maximum figure, the voltage drop across the a-c windings of the reactor is reduced to a low value such that the peak pulses of load current are not sufficient to satisfy the current equivalency relationship. This can be stated in another manner; namely, that for the specified magnetic amplifier, a proportional and linear relationship exists between load current and load voltage over a control current range from 0 to 22.5 milliamperes. When the control current is exceeded, the linearity ceases to exist, and further increases in control current do not produce corresponding increases in load current.

When plotted on the family of characteristic curves, the load line for lower values of load resistance more nearly approaches a vertical line. Thus a magnetic amplifier with a lower load resistance has a wider operating range of load current-load voltage linearity. With low load resistance, then, the control current can be varied between greater limits.

The selection of the actual load resistance in any given magnetic-amplifier circuit is determined by reference to the family of static curves. As mentioned previously, the lower portion of the load line must not intersect the $I_C = 0$ ma curve too near to the upward bend; if it does, small variations of supply voltage can produce large changes of load current. (This is particularly undesirable when feedback is used in the magnetic amplifier, as described in later chapters.) In addition, the upper portion of the load line must intersect the control characteristic just below the control signal limit. Thus, if the control current were not to exceed 25 milliamperes for a magnetic amplifier having the family of curves shown in Fig. 6-2, the upper portion of the load line would be selected to cut the $I_C = 22.5$ ma curve at point C, but not to cross the $I_C = 30$ ma curve.

As a further example, assume that the control current was not to exceed 12 milliamperes. The lower portion of the load line would be chosen to intersect the $I_C = 0$ curve at point F; the upper portion, however, would be selected to cross the $I_C = 15$ ma curve at point D but not to intersect the $I_C = 22.5$ ma curve. This load line is shown by the dashed line in Fig. 6-2, and represents a load resistance of approximately 900 ohms.

Although the operating point of the load line of Fig. 6-2 is shown at point F, it may be shifted to another point such as E by biasing the reactor. Bias is provided by applying the required voltage to a separate bias winding on the reactor or by superimposing the bias voltage on the control voltage in the common control winding. The magnetic flux produced in the presence of bias is the resultant of the fluxes produced by the bias and control currents. Shifting to point E would permit the control current to vary in both positive and negative directions around the operating point. In this manner, polarity-sensitive performance characteristics may be obtained.

6-4. Output (transfer) characteristics

The type of characteristic curve shown in Fig. 6-2 is by no means the only one that may be used to determine the operational aspects of a

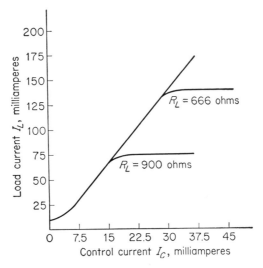

Fig. 6-3. Dynamic transfer (output) characteristics of a magnetic amplifier.

saturable-reactor circuit. An additional useful curve is obtained when load current I_L is plotted against control current I_C for different values of load resistance. This dynamic curve, shown in Fig. 6-3, may be derived from the static curves of Fig. 6-2 or may be obtained by laboratory techniques.

Two points are readily observable from the transfer curve of Fig. 6-3. In the first place, it is obvious that, with the exception of a small region near the origin, the load current is directly proportional to the control current up to a value determined by the load resistance. Thus, for $R_L = 900$ ohms, the $I_L I_c$ linearity exists up to approximately 15 milliamperes of control current, equal increments in control current producing approximately equal increments in load current. Above 15 milliamperes saturation may be considered as occurring so that the useful linearity relationship no longer exists. For $R_L = 666$ ohms, saturation occurs at a control current of approximately 25 milliamperes. Secondly, the characteristic curve does not begin at the origin, but rather intersects the ordinate above the origin. This is necessarily true, since with $I_C = 0$, the a-c windings of the saturable reactor will have a current flowing in them as determined by the applied voltage and the inductive reactance of the windings, or $I = E/X_L$. (This corresponds to the intersection of the load line with the $I_C = 0$ ma curve in Fig. 6-2.)

In reality, then, the total load current is the resultant of the current which flows in the absence of control voltage (this current may be designated as I_{L0}), and the current which flows as the result of the control voltage (this current may be designated as I_{LC}). Thus the total load current

$$I_L = I_{L0} + I_{LC} \tag{6-1}$$

It should be noted at this point that the load current flowing under no-signal conditions I_{L0} is sometimes called the *quiescent* (Q) *current* or the *standing current*.

The dynamic characteristic illustrated in Fig. 6-3 may be redrawn for a nonpolarized magnetic amplifier as shown in Fig. 6-4. The complete transfer characteristic is symmetrical; thus a positive control current of any value produces the same load current as a negative control current of the specified value.

With respect to Eq. (6-1) and Fig. 6-4, when $I_C = 0$, $I_L = I_{L0}$. When I_C increases to either a negative or positive value (negative or positive has meaning only with reference to the direction of current flow as determined by the polarity of the control voltage), I_L increases to $I_L = I_{L0} + I_{LC}$. The incremental increase in current represents the load current component which flows in response to the control current.

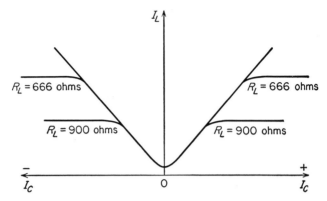

Fig. 6-4. Complete dynamic characteristics of a nonpolarized magnetic amplifier.

6-5. Multistage cascaded magnetic amplifiers

Magnetic amplifiers without feedback can be arranged in cascade in order to increase their useful sensitivity and power gain. A multistage circuit is shown in Fig. 6-5. In this circuit, the d-c input which might be supplied from batteries, thermocouples, photoelectric

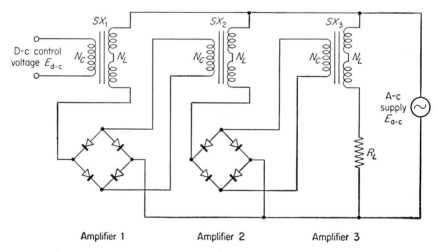

Fig. 6-5. Multistage cascaded magnetic amplifiers without compensation for quiescent load current effects.

cells, or from any other source is applied to the control winding of the input saturable reactor, the reactor of amplifier 1. The a-c supply voltage is applied to the load winding of this reactor and to the bridged dry-disc rectifiers of the first amplifier, so arranged that only a unidirectional current can flow in the N_c winding of the second reactor. The magnitude of this current is determined by the magnitude of the d-c input to the first reactor.

The a-c supply voltage is also applied to the load winding of the second reactor and to the bridged rectifiers of the second amplifier. The unidirectional current flowing in the control winding of the third reactor determines the impedance of the load winding of this reactor. The a-c supply voltage is applied to this load winding and to the series load. If desired, the load can be preceded by bridged rectifiers to convert the output into a d-c voltage.

In this multistage amplifier, small variations in the d-c input to the first amplifier stage produce sizable variations in output across the load. However, a definite limitation exists to the number of stages that can be cascaded in the simple manner shown in Fig. 6-5. This limitation results from the fact that even in the absence of d-c input to the first stage, a quiescent load current flows in the a-c winding of reactor 1, and rectified current flows in the control winding of reactor 2. Thus the core of reactor 2 will approach saturation, and will thereby deliver to the third stage a rectified current which exceeds that caused by the normal load current of the second stage. Each stage, in turn, will have its core saturated to a greater degree. Thus, if too many magnetic amplifiers are placed in cascade, the output stage will be fully saturated under conditions of no d-c input, and the introduction of input d-c control voltages will produce no effect in the output.

Cascaded magnetic amplifiers of the type shown in Fig. 6-5 are referred to as *uncompensated;* this means that no circuitry is included to eliminate the saturating effects produced by the quiescent load current which exists with no d-c input.

6-6. Compensation for quiescent load current effects

In order to prevent the saturation effects produced by the quiescent load current, *compensating circuits* are added to the non-feedback magnetic amplifiers. The purpose of the compensation is to reduce (or eliminate) the quiescent current component so that two or more non-feedback circuits can be connected in cascade (multistage) without the production of any undesired effects. One method of compensation used with multistage magnetic amplifiers is illustrated in Fig. 6-6. In this circuit, a center-tapped power transformer T_1 is used in conjunction with the a-c windings of the saturable reactors to form symmetrical bridge networks. To understand this, note that for amplifier 1, a bridge is formed by the center-tapped secondaries of T_1, the a-c wind-

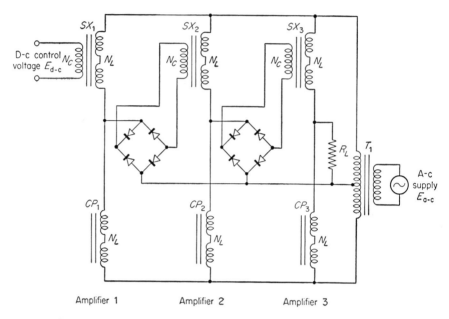

Fig. 6-6. Multistage cascaded magnetic amplifiers with bridge-type compensation to cancel quiescent current flow in load. (*After A. S. Fitz-Gerald, United States patent 2,027,311.*)

ings of the saturable reactor SX_1 and the a-c windings of counterpoise CP_1.* In reality, counterpoise CP_1 is identical to reactor SX_1 except that its control winding is left open. The important point is that the impedance of the a-c windings of SX_1 is identical to that of CP_1; if so desired, the counterpoise can be replaced by a choke of proper value. The rectifiers associated with amplifier 1 are connected between the center-tapped lead of the power transformer and the junction of SX_1 and CP_1.

Under conditions of zero d-c input, the impedance of SX_1 is equal to that of CP_1. Hence, the junction of CP_1 and SX_1 and the center-tapped transformer lead are equal potential points. Thus, no a-c voltage is applied to the rectifiers, and no rectified current flows in the

---

* The counterpoise for this purpose was first suggested by F. W. Lee, United States patent 1,855,639.

d-c winding of the saturable reactor of stage 2. Note, then, that compensation is complete for magnetic amplifier 1, and that in identical manner the quiescent load current is eliminated from the remaining stages.

When a d-c control voltage is applied to the input stage, the impedance of the load windings of SX_1 is decreased, and the bridge network now becomes unbalanced. The a-c difference of potential between the junction of SX_1 and CP_1 and the center-tapped transformer lead is applied to the rectifiers, and current flows in the control winding of SX_2. The process is repeated for magnetic amplifiers 2 and 3, so that under conditions of a small input control voltage, a large load-voltage variation appears. Saturation effects are eliminated by means of the described compensation networks.

A compensating network can be used in single-stage magnetic amplifier applications, in addition to its multistage uses. An example of such a circuit is that of Fig. 6-7. In this circuit, used for the measurement of direct currents, compensation for the quiescent current is necessary so that the electrodynamometer will indicate zero in the absence of a current to be measured.* However, when direct current is applied to the input control windings, the indicating instrument

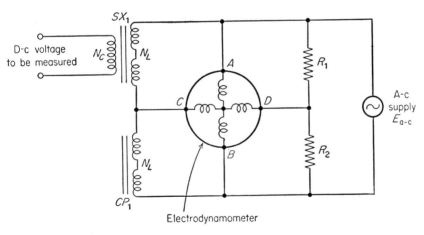

Fig. 6-7. Compensated symmetrical bridge circuit for direct-current measurement.

---

* The electrodynamometer is an instrument used for measuring currents. It consists of two vertical coils, one fixed in position, and the other turning about the vertical axis common to both. The deflection is determined by the current in the fixed and movable coils.

measures the value. The compensation in this case is accomplished by arranging the circuit into a symmetrical bridge network. The bridge comprises saturable reactor SX_1, counterpoise CP_1, and equal resistances R_1 and R_2. When the impedances of SX_1 and CP_1 are equal, as in the absence of a current to be measured, the bridge is balanced and no load current flows in the CD winding of the indicating instrument. (The AB winding, the excited winding, also has a current through it because it is connected across the a-c source.) When a current to be measured is applied to the control winding, the impedance of SX_1 changes, the bridge becomes unbalanced, and the electrodynamic instrument measures the increase in load current.

6-7. Polarity-sensitive magnetic amplifiers

The magnetic amplifiers discussed so far were of the nonpolarized type. The magnetic amplifier represented by the nonpolarized characteristic of Fig. 6-4 cannot distinguish between control currents of opposite polarity. The load current resulting from an increase in control current of one polarity would be equal to that produced by an equivalent increase in control current in the opposite direction.

For certain uses, it is desired that the magnetic amplifier be polarity-sensitive; that is, the magnetic amplifier should respond to direction as well as magnitude of the applied control current. Amplifiers of this type are said to be *polarized*, and may have an asymmetrical transfer characteristic such as is shown in Fig. 6-8. Examining this curve, it can be seen that the load current produced by a fixed value of negative control current will be different from that produced by a positive control current of the same value. In effect, the load current starts at a low value for negative values of control current, and increases to a peak as the control current decreases from this negative value to zero and increases in the positive direction.

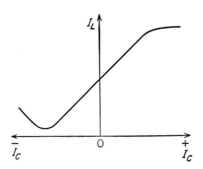

Fig. 6-8. Asymmetrical transfer characteristics of a polarity-sensitive magnetic amplifier.

An asymmetrical transfer characteristic can be produced by the use of a bias winding on the saturable reactor [Fig. 6-9(a)], or by providing a steady current, in addition to the control current, in the control

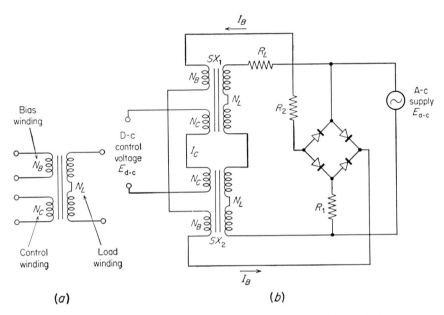

Fig. 6-9. (a) Schematic symbol of magnetic amplifier with bias winding. (b) Biased, balanced magnetic amplifier that responds to control-winding polarity variations.

winding. In either case, the bias produced will provide the magnetic amplifier with discrimination between positive and negative signals, so that a positive control signal causes an increased output while a negative control signal reduces the output.

Figure 6-9(b) represents a polarized magnetic amplifier that uses separate bias windings on the reactors. The addition of bias shifts the effective operating point on the load line (as from point F in Fig. 6-2 to point E). As a result, an asymmetrical transfer characteristic similar to that shown in Fig. 6-8 is produced. It can be seen that the load current never changes its direction; its magnitude, however, increases as the positive control current increases. To understand the circuit operation of the polarized magnetic amplifier [Fig. 6-9(b)], note that the a-c supply voltage is not only applied to the load windings of reactors SX_1 and SX_2 in series with load resistor R_L, but is also applied to the bridge rectifiers. The rectifiers permit a unidirectional bias current I_B to flow in the direction indicated through R_2, through the bias windings N_B of reactors SX_1 and SX_2, and through R_1. The magnitude of the bias current is proportional to the supply voltage, and produces a steady core magnetization of a fixed value.

When control current is applied to the circuit, the degree of core magnetization will change, increasing if the magnetic fields produced by I_B and I_C are in phase, and decreasing if they oppose. It now becomes evident that the polarity of the control current, as well as its magnitude, will control the amount of load current in the magnetic amplifier. This, then, is the essence of a polarized magnetic amplifier.

Figure 6-10 represents another polarized amplifier which uses bias but does not use separate bias windings. In this circuit, the bias cur-

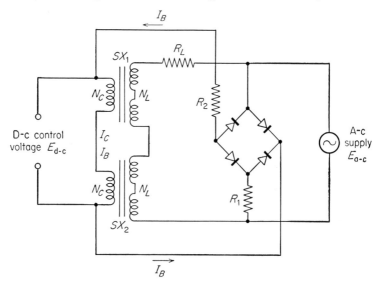

Fig. 6-10. Polarity-sensitive magnetic amplifier with control windings acting as bias windings.

rent produced by the full-wave rectifiers flows through the control windings of the two reactors, as does the actual control current. In effect, then, the control windings are serving for both control and bias purposes. The remaining operation of the circuit is the same as that of Fig. 6-9(b).

6-8. Balanced push-pull magnetic amplifiers

The nonpolarized magnetic amplifier of Art. 6-2 could not discriminate between control currents of opposite polarities. The polarized magnetic amplifier of Art. 6-7 could distinguish between control current polarities but only in such a manner as to change the magnitude of a load current without changing its direction. The *push-pull magnetic amplifier** can not only distinguish control current polarity but can also cause the load current to change in direction, in accordance with the control current direction. The amplifier transfer characteristic is illustrated in Fig. 6-11(a). Note that with $I_C = 0$, $I_L = 0$. When the control current increases in a positive direction, the

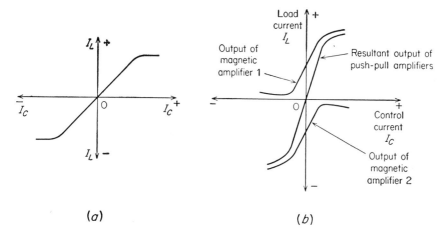

(*a*)   (*b*)

Fig. 6-11. (a) Transfer characteristics of a push-pull magnetic amplifier. (b) Derivation of push-pull characteristic curve.

load current increases in a positive direction; when I_C moves in a negative direction, I_L follows suit.

The push-pull magnetic amplifier has certain outstanding characteristics. For one, it provides a duo-directional output, with a zero output occurring in the absence of control voltage. Secondly, it has good stability, with voltage variations in both sections canceling each other out. In addition, the linear range area over which the device operates is extended beyond that of a single-ended unit. The derivation of the push-pull curve is shown in Fig. 6-11(b).

A push-pull magnetic amplifier circuit is illustrated in Fig. 6-12. In this case, the magnetic amplifier comprises two equal saturable reactors SX_1 and SX_2, each having a bias winding N_B, a control winding N_C, and a load winding N_L. The bias voltage is applied to the bias

---

* Sometimes called duo-directional magnetic amplifier.

windings connected in series such that each saturable reactor is operating an equal amount off its zero operating point. In other words, the bias voltage chooses the operating point of each unit for zero control signal. In the absence of control voltage, and on the half-cycle when the a-c supply voltage has the indicated polarity, electrons

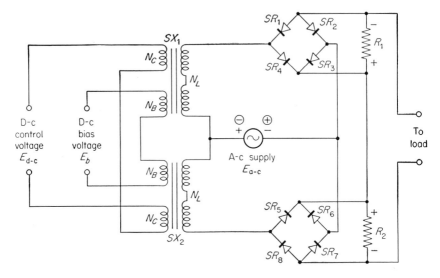

Fig. 6-12. Push-pull magnetic amplifier.

flow from the negative potential point of the supply through the load winding N_L of reactor SX_1, rectifier SR_1, resistor R_1, and rectifier SR_3 back to the positive potential point. On this same half-cycle, electrons flow in similar manner through the balanced network consisting of the load winding N_L of reactor SX_2, rectifier SR_8, resistor R_2, and rectifier SR_6. On the next half-cycle, rectifiers SR_2 and SR_4 conduct in the upper portion of the circuit, and SR_5 and SR_7 conduct in the lower portion. The voltage developed across R_1 and R_2 remain the same as they were on the first half-cycle.

In the absence of control voltage, an equal but opposite a-c current is forced through both N_L windings of the saturable reactors and through their associated external resistors R_1 and R_2. Because both reactors have an equal impedance at this time, the voltages developed across these resistors are equal but opposite, and so cancel each other. No output load voltage is forthcoming under these conditions.

When direct control current of a specified polarity flows through the series opposing control windings of saturable reactors SX_1 and SX_2, the d-c core flux produced will aid the flux produced by one of the reactor load windings while opposing that produced by the other. As a result, the voltage developed across one of the external resistors will increase while the other decreases, and a resultant load output voltage of definite polarity appears. When the control current polarity is reversed, the entire operation reverses and a load output voltage of the opposite polarity is developed. Thus, since the two external resistors R_1 and R_2 are backing each other, the resultant output is a function of both control-current magnitude and polarity.

In certain applications, the resistors R_1 and R_2 are replaced by two equal windings (as in the case of a relay, solenoid, or machine field). In this arrangement, the fluxes produced by the two equal windings buck each other in producing the resultant magnetomotive force. As described for the circuit containing resistors (Fig. 6-12), the resultant flux is a function of both the magnitude and polarity of the applied control voltage.

6-9. Magnetic amplifier power gains

In magnetic amplifiers, the power gain is dependent to a great degree upon the design, type, and physical size of the reactor device. For typical magnetic amplifiers of the varieties described, the gain figures per stage varied from about 10 to 100. Power gain is, of course, the ratio between output power and input power. In a magnetic amplifier, the output power is considered as that power developed in the load windings and delivered to the load; the input power is that developed in the control windings. Since power is equivalent to I^2R, the power gain for a magnetic amplifier, when the impedance of the load equals that of the output windings of the reactor, can be shown as

$$\text{power gain (no feedback) } K_P = \frac{\text{power output}}{\text{power input}} = \frac{I_L^2 R_L}{I_C^2 R_C} \qquad (6\text{-}2)$$

where I_L = current in the load windings
I_C = current in the control windings
R_L = resistance of the load
R_C = resistance of the control windings.

Because of the current transformer characteristics of the reactor, the currents are inversely proportional to the turns ratio, so that Eq. (6-2) can be converted to

$$\text{power gain (no feedback) } K_P = \frac{N_c^2 R_L}{N_L^2 R_c} \tag{6-3}$$

where N_C = number of turns in the control winding
N_L = number of turns in the load winding.

With reference to either Eq. (6-2) or (6-3), it is evident that an increase in the value of load resistance will produce an increased power gain. It is obvious, however, that an increase of this type will continue only within the limits set by the physical design of the saturable reactor, and that an attempted increase beyond these limits will, in effect, produce a reduced gain.

Another means for producing increased gains is by connecting magnetic amplifiers in cascade. The primary disadvantage of this method is that additional component parts are required. Many modern magnetic amplifiers use regenerative feedback to increase the gain of the single stage. This technique is described in Chapter 8.

6-10. Variable-gain push-pull magnetic amplifier

The gain of a magnetic amplifier can be varied, if it is so desired, by means of a push-pull circuit similar to that shown in Fig. 6-13. When the magnitude of the d-c voltage applied to control windings of

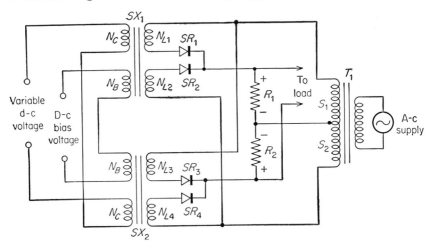

Fig. 6-13. Variable-gain push-pull magnetic amplifier.

the reactors is varied, the magnetic amplifier output appearing across resistors R_1 and R_2 and applied to the load is changed. The output of this circuit can be changed from zero in either direction.

The a-c supply voltage is applied to the primary of transformer T_1, which is equipped with a center-tapped secondary winding (for convenience labeled S_1 and S_2). Assume initially that the bias and control windings of the reactors have no effect. When the voltage appearing across the S_1 winding is such that the center-tap is negative with respect to the outer end, electrons flow through resistor R_1, rectifier SR_1, and load winding N_{L1} (SX_1), and equally through resistor R_2, rectifier SR_3, and load winding N_{L3}. On the next half-cycle when the center-tap is negative with respect to the outer end of the S_2 winding, electrons flow through R_2, SR_4, and N_{L4} (SX_2) and equally through R_1, SR_2, and N_{L2} (SX_1). Under these conditions, the voltages across resistors R_1 and R_2 are equal and opposite and no output appears across the load.

The condition of zero output will further be obtained when the fixed d-c voltage applied to the bias windings produces a flux which is completely offset by the flux produced by the variable voltage applied to the control windings. When this variable voltage is changed from the value, in either direction, the impedances of the load windings of the two reactors are no longer equal, and output appears across the load. As indicated previously, the load voltage can be either positive or negative, as determined solely by the relationship between the bias winding and control winding fluxes.

REVIEW QUESTIONS

1. A magnetic amplifier has a control resistance of 500 ohms and a load resistance of 100,000 ohms. If 50 milliamperes of current flow in the control circuit and 10 milliamperes in the load circuit, what is the power gain of the amplifier?

2. With reference to Eq. (6-3), if the control windings in a magnetic amplifier are doubled, and all other circuit factors remain constant, what happens to the power gain of the device?

3. In the circuit shown in Fig. 6-6, the gain of amplifier 1 is 12, the gain of amplifier 2 is 20, and the gain of amplifier 3 is 15. What is the over-all gain of the cascaded device?

4. In the circuit of Fig. 6-12, which of the rectifiers are conducting simultaneously? (Determine this by assuming an a-c supply polarity, and observing the circuit operation.)

5. What are the advantages of using balanced push-pull magnetic amplifiers?

6. Describe a circuit application in which it would be desirable to use a magnetic amplifier that is polarity-sensitive.

CHAPTER

7

Applications of Magnetic

Amplifiers without Feedback

7-1. Introduction

The magnetic amplifier without feedback, like the saturable re-actor, is the predecessor of the more sophisticated magnetic amplifier with feedback. Despite its relative simplicity, the non-feedback magnetic amplifier has great versatility, and is used in many important applications. Again, the circuits illustrated in this chapter are meant only to be representative examples of those encountered in industry.

7-2. Magnetic amplifier control of d-c motor speed

One of the most important and useful applications of the magnetic amplifier has been in the control of the d-c motor, particularly of its speed. To vary the speed of a shunt-excited d-c motor* requires

---

* The type most commonly used in industry for driving applications.

that the voltage across its field or the voltage across its armature be variable. The speed of a shunt-excited motor is given by

$$S = \frac{E - IR}{k\Phi} \qquad (7\text{-}1)$$

where S = speed of motor
E = voltage across armature
I = current through armature
R = resistance of armature
k = coefficient of proportionality
Φ = magnetic flux produced by shunt field.

With reference to this equation, it can be noted that the motor speed can be controlled by varying the armature voltage or by changing the magnetic field strength of the shunt field. Thus the motor speed will increase if the armature voltage is increased or if the voltage applied to the shunt field is decreased.

An elementary method for controlling motor speed by means of field flux variation is shown in Fig. 7-1. The saturable reactor used in this application is equipped with four windings: a bias winding N_B; a

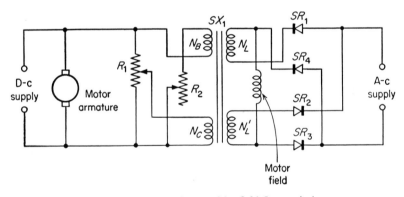

Fig. 7-1. Motor speed control by field flux variation.

control winding N_C wound opposite to the bias winding; and two equal but opposite load windings N_L and N_L'. The a-c supply is rectified by copper oxide rectifiers SR_1 through SR_4, so that a direct current flows through the motor field winding. When the top end of the a-c line in Fig. 7-1 is negative, electrons flow through SR_2, load winding N_L', the motor field, and SR_4 to the positive end of the line. On the next half-cycle, electrons flow through SR_3, the motor field (in the same direction as previously), the other load winding N_L, and SR_1

to the positive end of the line. The voltage developed across the field is dependent, of course, upon the impedance of the reactor load windings.

A constant d-c voltage from a separate supply is applied to the motor armature. This same voltage also appears across bias winding N_B in series with rheostat R_2. Basically this winding determines the point of core saturation around which the circuit operation fluctuates. The d-c supply is also applied to potentiometer R_1. The position of the movable arm of this potentiometer determines the voltage applied to, and the current flowing in, the control winding N_C of the reactor, and thereby ultimately controls the motor speed. When the arm is at the top of the potentiometer (Fig. 7-1), maximum current flows in the control winding of the reactor. Since the control winding is connected opposite to the bias winding, it causes the core flux to move in a direction away from core saturation. As a result, the load windings offer maximum impedance at this time, so that minimum voltage is developed across the motor field, causing the motor speed to be at maximum. The opposite action occurs when the arm of the potentiometer short-circuits the control winding; in this case, maximum field flux is obtained, and the motor speed is reduced.

Although not shown in Fig. 7-1, a centrifugal switch is mounted on the motor switch, and acts to short-circuit potentiometer R_2 when the motor is started, until the motor has reached a minimum speed. In this way, a large bias voltage is produced initially, thereby guaranteeing that the operating field will be large as the motor starts. When the motor speed has increased above a specified minimum value, which is within the control range, the centrifugal switch opens and the bias decreases to a level determined by potentiometer R_2. From this point on, the setting of potentiometer R_1 sets the motor speed.

The magnetic amplifier may also be used to regulate the speed of a motor by controlling the voltage across the armature. This method is preferable to the field control described, since inherently it allows a much wider range of speed control. An elementary circuit for this performance is shown in Fig. 7-2. The a-c supply voltage is rectified by copper-oxide rectifiers SR_1 through SR_4 arranged such that a d-c voltage appears across the motor armature. When the upper end of the a-c line is negative, electrons flow through SR_2, load winding N_L', the armature, and SR_4, completing the circuit. When, on the next half-cycle, the lower end of the line is negative, electrons flow through SR_3, the armature, the other load winding N_L, and SR_1, completing the circuit. Thus the voltage appearing across the armature is a rectified voltage. The magnitude of this voltage is dependent upon the impedance of the load windings.

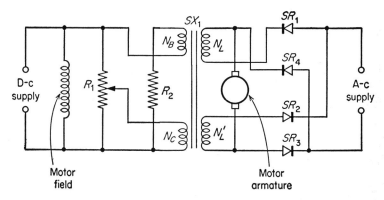

Fig. 7-2. Motor speed control by armature voltage variation.

The d-c supply is applied directly to the motor field winding, so that the operating flux is constant. This voltage also appears across potentiometer R_1, the arm of which controls the voltage applied to, and consequently the current that flows in, the control winding. When the arm is in the uppermost position (Fig. 7-2), the impedance of the load windings is at its minimum. Consequently, the voltage across the armature is at its maximum, and the motor rotates at top speed. The winding N_B biases the reactor so that unidirectional, rather than duo-directional, control currents will be effective. This winding has the same function as in the circuit of Fig. 7-1.

Although the motor-control circuits described thus far regulated either the armature voltage or the field flux, it must not be taken for granted that the two types of motor control are necessarily exclusive of each other. In actuality, many automatic motor-control circuits use both systems interdependently. In this manner, the accurate speed control and versatile motor operation required for modern machine drives are forthcoming.

7-3. Magnetic amplifier generator voltage regulation

Another typical application of the non-feedback magnetic amplifier is its use as a voltage regulator. In this case the output of a generator and the output of a reference voltage supply are applied in opposition across a reactor control winding N_C. When these voltages are not equal it implies that the generator output has strayed from the level set up by the reference voltage supply. The error voltage across the N_C winding produced in this instance will change the impedance of the load windings in such a direction as to cause the operating field flux to minimize the error voltage. In effect, the change in flux changes the generator output until it agrees with the reference.

The reference voltage for this circuit may be supplied by a voltage stabilizer or from a regulated d-c power supply or the like. The reference voltage is generally placed across a potentiometer, thus permitting a choice of magnitude for the regulated voltage. The elementary regulator circuit, with but slight modifications, can be used to regulate the output voltage of an a-c generator or alternator (the alternator output is rectified and then compared with the d-c reference voltage); to regulate the direct current of a generator; to regulate the speed of a motor. Thus the circuit may be considered as basic, and easily modified to suit the requirements of a given application.

7-4. Temperature control using magnetic amplifier

When the magnetic amplifier is applied to a temperature-control system, it may operate on the basis of a voltage variation as obtained, for example, from a thermocouple, or on the basis of a resistance change as produced, for example, by a thermistor. A temperature control system using a thermistor* is illustrated in Fig. 7-3. In this system, a heating element located in a furnace is used to maintain the oven temperature at a specified level. The a-c supply voltage is applied to the bridge rectifier network comprising rectifiers SR_1 through SR_4, equal reactor load windings N_L and N'_L, and the heating element. The potential developed across the element determines the heat it radiates, and therefore the furnace temperature it produces. When the reactor core saturation level is determined solely by the flux produced by the bias winding N_B, as when the direct current in the

---

* The thermistor (or thermal resistor) is a solid conductor made of various combinations of manganese, nickel, cobalt, and other metallic oxides. It has a negative temperature coefficient; that is, its resistance varies inversely with temperature. The thermistor is manufactured in bead, disc, or rod form. The variations in temperature which bring about the resistance changes may be produced externally, as by changes in the surrounding air or water, internally, by the current through the thermistor, or indirectly by means of a heating coil surrounding the thermistor element.

control winding is zero or a low value, the impedance of the reactor is relatively low, a relatively small portion of the a-c supply appears across the equal load windings, and a large amount of rectified voltage

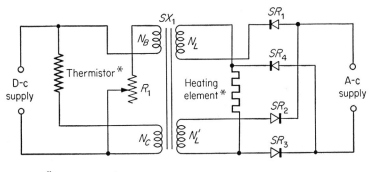

* Both located in oven

Fig. 7-3. Magnetic amplifier in temperature control system.

is developed across the heating element. The temperature level is relatively high at this time.

The thermistor is connected in series with the control winding of the saturable reactor, and placed across a d-c source. Since the thermistor is physically located within the furnace, temperature variations within the oven limit the thermistor's resistance, and thereby control the heat produced by the heating element. To follow this, assume that the furnace temperature has started to increase. The ambient temperature of the air around the thermistor also increases, so that the thermistor resistance decreases. As a result, the current through the control winding becomes larger. Because the control winding is connected opposite to the bias winding, the core saturation level now diminishes. In turn, the impedance of the load windings increases, and less rectified voltage appears across the heating element. Consequently, the furnace temperature increase is offset by the decreased heating effect. The converse action occurs, of course, when the temperature decreases below a set level.

The use of a temperature-control system based on resistance changes (Fig. 7-3) is normally preferred to one predicated on thermocouple voltage variations because larger control signals are obtained by the former method. However, if a thermocouple voltage is to be used as the controlling element in the circuit, a multistage magnetic-amplifier circuit using push-pull stages can be applied. A circuit of this type is shown in Fig. 7-4. In this thermocouple-controlled magnetic amplifier, the circuit consists of two separate push-pull magnetic amplifiers, made of saturable reactors SX_1 and SX_2. Reactor

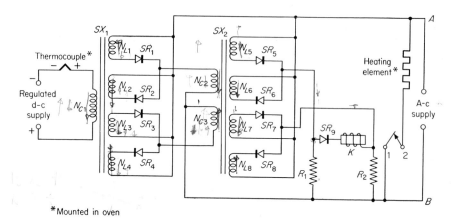

* Mounted in oven

Fig. 7-4. Multistage magnetic-amplifier thermocouple temperature control.

SX_1 comprises load windings N_{L1} through N_{L4} and single control winding N_{C1}. Reactor SX_2 comprises load windings N_{L5} through N_{L8} and oppositely connected control windings N_{C2} and N_{C3}.

To follow the circuit operation, assume initially that the control winding N_{C1} (SX_1) has no effect upon operation. The a-c supply voltage is applied to the load windings of saturable reactor SX_1 which are connected in series with the dual control windings of reactor SX_2. On one half of the a-c cycle (when point A is negative), electrons flow through N_{L2}, SR_2, and N_{C2} as well as through parallel path N_{L4}, SR_4, and N_{C3}. On the second half-cycle (when point B is negative), electrons flow through N_{C2}, SR_1, and N_{L2} in parallel with N_{C3}, SR_3 and N_{L3}. Because the currents are equal, the fluxes produced by the oppositely wound control windings N_{C2} and N_{C3} cancel during both half-cycles, so that saturable reactor SX_2 operates in the vicinity of zero core saturation.

On the half-cycle when point A is negative, the SX_2 electron flow is through N_{L6}, SR_6, and R_1 in parallel with N_{L8}, SR_8, and R_2; on the next half-cycle, the paths are through R_1, SR_5, and N_{L5} in parallel with R_2, SR_7, and N_{L7}. Since equal potentials are developed across resistors R_1 and R_2, relay coil K is not actuated, and normally closed contacts 1 and 2 complete the electric heating-element circuit in the furnace.

A regulated d-c voltage is applied to control winding N_{C1} of SX_1. The core flux produced by this winding is of fixed direction, and as such will aid the flux produced by the load windings of one portion of the reactor while opposing that produced by the other windings. As a result, the output of one portion of the reactor applied to the control windings of SX_2 will increase, while the other necessarily decreases. This variation, in turn, will be amplified by SX_2.

The thermocouple is connected such that its output opposes the reference voltage. In operation, then, as the furnace temperature increases, the thermocouple output increases, and in effect modulates the flux produced by saturable reactor SX_1. The SX_1 impedance variation produced as a result changes the current through N_{C2} and N_{C3}, and the output is further amplified by SX_2. Thus, relay K is actuated, opening the heating circuit of the furnace, and thereby causing the oven temperature to decrease to its desired level.

7-5. Control of two-phase servo motor

The two-phase induction motor is used extensively in high-performance servomechanisms because of the advantages it affords. Control of this type of motor can be accomplished by the magnetic-amplifier circuit shown in Fig. 7-5. In this circuit, the variable control

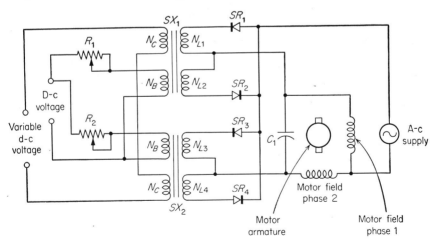

Fig. 7-5. Magnetic amplifier control of a two-phase servo motor.

voltage is applied to the N_C windings of the saturable reactors, thereby simultaneously varying the current in, and the flux produced around, the two motor fields. Capacitor C_1 is used for phasing purposes so that the currents in the motor windings are approximately 90 degrees out of phase with respect to each other. This is a basic requirement for the operation of a two-phase induction-type reversible motor.

Magnetic amplifier servo systems and applications are described in detail in Chapter 10.

7-6. Harmonic amplifier circuits

In the applications described thus far in this chapter, the frequency of the alternating output current was the same as that of the a-c supply voltage. However, the devices may be so connected as to emphasize the production of the higher harmonics in the output winding. Circuitry of this type may be used in resistance welding applications; for example, 3-phase, 50-cycle power is used to produce 1-phase, 100-cycle power. Harmonic amplifier circuits have proved to be useful in the conversion of small d-c voltages into highly stable a-c voltages, as in null detectors, magnetometers, and magnetic modulators.

Figure 7-6(a) illustrates two saturable reactors connected so as to emphasize the generation of second-harmonic currents in the load circuit. Each reactor has a control winding (N_C) to which d-c power is applied, and two a-c windings (N_L and N'_L), with a-c power applied

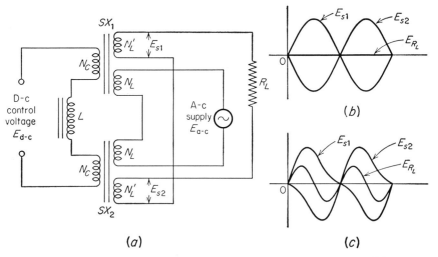

(a)   (b)   (c)

Fig. 7-6. (a) Harmonic amplification using saturable reactors. (b) Secondary voltage in absence of control voltage. (c) Secondary voltages in presence of control voltage.

to one (N_L) and second-harmonic power taken from the second (N'_L). When no control current is permitted to flow in the control windings, the voltages induced from the N_L to the N'_L windings by the supply voltage are equal and opposite, thereby producing load currents which cancel in the output circuit. This cancellation will occur despite any variations in the supply voltage. When control current of any given polarity flows in the N_C windings, the magnetic flux produced will aid the a-c flux in one reactor, while concurrently opposing the a-c flux in the other. As a result, the voltages induced into the N'_L windings are no longer equal and opposite, but are rather highly asymmetrical. The resultant load voltage (the difference between the N'_L voltage of SX_1 and N'_L voltage of SX_2) contains the desired second-harmonic power.*

This operation can be understood further by reference to Fig. 7-6 (b) and (c). In (b), which shows the waveforms existing in the absence of control current, the secondary voltages E_{s1} and E_{s2} are of equal amplitude but opposite phase. The resultant load voltage is zero, as evidenced by the straight line. Fig. 7-6(c) illustrates the situation when control current flows. Now E_{s1} and E_{s2} are asymmetrical, producing a resultant second-harmonic voltage.

Inductor L in Fig. 7-6(a) offers high impedance to harmonic currents, thereby effectively preventing them from being induced into the control windings. In the absence of the choke, the control circuit would act as a short circuit insofar as second-harmonic power was concerned.

Although the control voltage of Fig. 7-6(a) is indicated to be of fixed polarity, this is not necessarily the case; it may be of varying polarity. A d-c polarity reversal produces a second-harmonic voltage of opposite phase. Specifically, with reference to the second-harmonic waveform of Fig. 7-6(c), this voltage is positive on the first half-cycle and negative on the second. If the control current were reversed, the second harmonic would be of opposite phase, namely it would be negative on the first half-cycle and positive on the second. Basically, then, the harmonics reverse their phase when the d-c magnetic flux changes in direction. This permits the circuit to be applied to the detection and amplification of small d-c voltages obtainable, for example, from thermocouples.

---

* To be more accurate, the load voltage produced is rich in all even harmonics, primarily the second, of course. In certain instances, a resonant circuit is used in conjunction with the load to emphasize the desired second harmonic.

Another form of second-harmonic amplifier circuit, which might be considered as a magnetic modulator, is illustrated in Fig. 7-7. The a-c supply voltage is applied to the center-tapped primary windings of transformer T_1 and to the load windings N_L of saturable reactors SX_1 and SX_2. In the absence of d-c control voltage, the voltages across the N_L windings are equal and opposite so that no a-c voltage appears across the secondary winding of T_1.

When current flows in the control windings of the reactors, the impedance of one reactor increases during one-half cycle, while that of

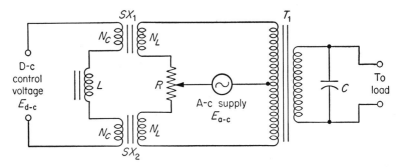

Fig. 7-7. Magnetic modulator using saturable reactor.

the second decreases at the same time. As a result, an a-c voltage appears across the secondary of the transformer. Capacitor C resonates the secondary to the secondary harmonic of the source voltage. This output can then be applied to a conventional amplifier, the output of which, in turn, may be used to control a load. Inductor L offers a high impedance to harmonic voltages, thereby suppressing them so far as the control windings are concerned. Potentiometer R is used for zero adjustment in the absence of d-c input voltage.

7-7. Magnetic amplifier discriminator

The magnetic amplifier can be connected to discriminate between signals of the same frequency but of different phase. In such a circuit, a d-c output voltage of given polarity is produced when a specific phase relationship exists between the two signals. When this phase relationship reverses, the polarity of the d-c voltage reverses.

To follow the circuit action of the discriminator shown in Fig. 7-8, assume that no a-c signal is applied to the control windings and that the a-c supply is on the half-cycle shown by the circled polarity. At this time, electrons flow through rectifier SR_2, load winding N_L'' of reactor SX_1, and resistor R_1, and simultaneously through rectifier SR_4, load winding N_L'' of reactor SX_2, and resistor R_2. The voltages

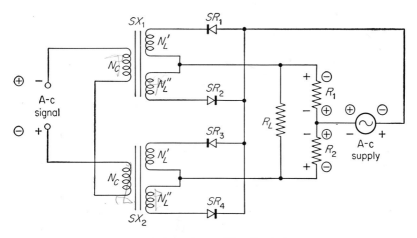

Fig. 7-8. Magnetic amplifier discriminator.

developed across R_1 and R_2 are of the circled polarity; since they are equal in addition to being opposite, they cancel so that no voltage appears across load R_L. The same action occurs on the next half-cycle; again, equal but opposite voltages appear across R_1 and R_2, canceling across R_L.

Assume now that a-c signal of fixed phase with respect to the supply voltage is applied to the control windings of the reactors. If both the a-c signal and the a-c supply are operating on the half-cycle having the circled polarity, the flux produced around the control windings will drive the core of SX_1 into saturation rapidly, and will, at the same time, reduce the flux in the SX_2 core. As a result, the impedance of SX_1 decreases and that of SX_2 increases, so that the voltage across R_1 increases and that across R_2 decreases. A resultant voltage appears across the load R_L.

Similar operation occurs on the next half-cycle. Thus, as long as the phase between signal and supply remains constant, a d-c voltage of constant polarity and fixed average magnitude exists across the load. If, however, the phase relationship between the two signals reverses, the polarity of the d-c voltage will also change. Thus, the circuit is capable of distinguishing between different phase relationships.

REVIEW QUESTIONS

1. Explain the operation of the circuit illustrated in Fig. 7-1 when the arms of potentiometer R_1 and R_2 are: (a) both at the top; (b) both at the bottom; (c) R_1 at the top and R_2 at the bottom; and (d) R_1 at the bottom and R_2 at the top.

2. The thermocouple of Fig. 7-5 is connected such that its output opposes the reference voltage. What would occur if the thermocouple were connected such that its output aided, rather than opposed, the reference voltage? Explain your answer.

3. What are the functions of potentiometers R_1 and R_2 in Fig. 7-5? Describe the circuit operation for different settings of these potentiometers.

4. The potentiometer in Fig. 7-7 is used to zero-adjust the magnetic amplifier in the absence of control voltage. What might occur if this adjustment were not made?

CHAPTER

8

The Magnetic Amplifier with External Feedback

▄▄

8-1. Introduction

Modern magnetic-amplifier practice requires that maximum gain be obtained in a single stage, where possible. This can be accomplished by *positive* or *regenerative feedback* — i.e., feeding a portion of the output power back into the input circuit, in such phase that the output assists the control input. In this way, the actual value of power gain can be increased without resorting to a change in the optimum value of load resistance.

When the feedback is accomplished by means of an external inductively coupled winding which is not an inherent part of the basic magnetic amplifier, it may be referred to as *external* or *extrinsic* feedback. Most regenerative feedbacks are of this type. In these circuits, rectified load current flows through the feedback windings. In the presence of feedback, the control characteristic changes as shown in Fig. 8-1(a). Note that the curve is no longer symmetrical; with feedback, the load current reaches a minimum at a small negative control signal.

Feedback can also be accomplished by having the load current directly produce feedback of proper phase in the control circuit. This is referred to as *internal*, *intrinsic*, *electric*, or *self-saturated* feedback. In

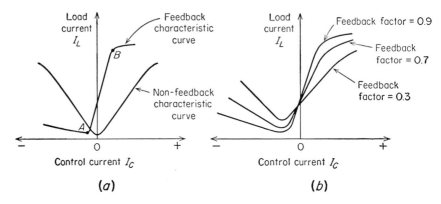

Fig. 8-1. (a) Comparison of control characteristics of feedback and non-feedback magnetic amplifiers.   (b) Control characteristics with different amounts of feedback.

circuits using this type of feedback, a rectifier is connected in series with the load so that direct current, proportional to the mean value of the load current, flows through the load windings.

External feedback does not affect the value of the input-circuit impedance; that is, the apparent resistance of the control circuit. Positive internal feedback increases the input impedance, while negative internal feedback decreases it. However, as long as the input impedance remains relatively low, the feedback amplifier operates in similar fashion to the non-feedback device, except that the presence of feedback reduces the number of control windings required to maintain control over a fixed number of load windings. In any case, the waveforms of the feedback amplifier are the same as those of the non-feedback amplifier.

The amount of feedback will determine the final shape of the characteristic curve, as shown in Fig. 8-1(b). Note that as the feedback is increased, the slope of the portion of the curve in the positive control region increases, while that portion of the curve in the negative region decreases. Thus, increases in the amount of regenerative feedback lead to increases in gain.

8-2. Gains of feedback amplifiers

The current equivalency relationship for the magnetic amplifier without feedback was given as

$$N_C I_C = N_L I_L \qquad (4\text{-}1)$$

When regenerative feedback is added, this relationship is modified to become

$$N_C I_C + N_F I_F = N_L I_L \qquad (8\text{-}1)$$

where N_F = number of turns in the feedback winding
I_F = current flowing in the feedback winding.

Solving Eq. (8-1), we have

$$N_C I_C = N_L I_L - N_F I_F \qquad (8\text{-}1a)$$

$$N_C I_C = N_L I_L \left(1 - N_F I_F / N_L I_L\right) \qquad (8\text{-}2)$$

Thus, solving for the current gain, K_I, i.e., the ratio between I_L and I_C,

$$K_I = \frac{I_L}{I_C} = \frac{N_C}{N_L} \left(\frac{1}{1 - N_F I_F / N_L I_L}\right) \qquad (8\text{-}2a)$$

For the magnetic amplifier with series-connected load windings, it can be assumed that $I_F = I_L$. As a result, Eq. (8-2a) resolves to

$$K_I = \frac{I_L}{I_C} = \frac{N_C}{N_L} \left(\frac{1}{1 - N_F / N_L}\right) \qquad (8\text{-}2b)$$

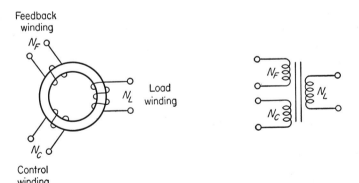

Fig. 8-2. Graphical and schematic symbols of reactor with feedback winding.

The denominator $(1 - N_F / N_L)$ in this equation is the feedback factor. When $N_F = 0$, the case for a non-feedback amplifier, Eq.

(8-2b) reduces to Eq. (4-1). When for a regenerative amplifier, the ratio N_F/N_L approaches 1, the current gain of the device — i.e., the ratio between I_L and I_C — increases. (When the term equals 1, the gain is infinite but the circuit is highly unstable.) In the presence of degenerative feedback, the final denominator in Eq. (8-2b) becomes $1 + N_F/N_L$. Under this condition, the current gain of the device is reduced.

The power gain without feedback is given by Eq. (6-3). In the presence of regenerative feedback, this becomes

$$\text{power gain (positive feedback) } K_P = \frac{N_C^2 R_L}{N_L^2 R_C} \left(\frac{1}{1 - N_F/N_L} \right)^2 \quad (8\text{-}3)$$

where N_C = number of turns in the control winding
N_L = number of turns in the load winding
N_F = number of turns in the feedback winding.

Again note that the important term of this equation is $\dfrac{1}{1 - N_F/N_L}$.*

As the turns ratio of the feedback winding to the load winding approaches unity, the denominator of the term approaches zero, and the term itself becomes increasingly large. In a non-feedback magnetic amplifier, $N_F = 0$, and Eq. (8-3) resolves itself into Eq. (6-3).

In many instances, external feedback magnetic amplifiers are connected in cascade. The total power gain of the over-all circuit, which is the ratio between the output power of the final stage and the input power to the first stage, often runs to 10^6 or greater. The advantage of cascading does not lie so much in the large gains derived as it does in the increased *figure of merit* of the amplifier. The figure of merit is defined as the ratio of the power gain to the speed of response in cycles per second, and may be as low as 4 or 5 in the basic non-feedback circuit.

It will be recalled that the basic non-feedback amplifier has a definite limitation as to its speed of response. The power control action of the device — i.e., its action in controlling the deliverable output power — is preceded by a period during which the device establishes the control level. This level is usually set during a time equal to one half-cycle of the a-c source voltage, and the output power is generally delivered during an equal time. If the control and output

---

* This term, for a degenerative feedback amplifier, becomes $\dfrac{1}{1 + N_F/N_L}$.

periods are both less than one half-cycle, as they may be, this will produce the minimum delay possible. However, the figure of merit will necessarily be low, because of the low power gain.

To increase the figure of merit, feedback amplifiers of nominal gain (200 to 1000) are connected in cascade. Although the total power gain of stages in cascade is the product of the individual stage gains, the total time constant (speed of response) of stages so connected is the sum of the time constants of each stage. Thus, increasing the stages increases the ratio between the power gain and the time constant, causing the figure of merit to assume values of 5000 or more.

8-3. Operation of the regenerative feedback amplifier

The operation of the regenerative feedback magnetic amplifier may also be explained by reference to the amplifier characteristic curve, Fig. 8-1(a). This figure illustrates the load current I_L, plotted against the control current I_C, for a regenerative feedback amplifier. Note that when $I_C = 0$, a definite load current will flow. This load current is the quiescent current of the magnetic amplifier.

When the control current is increased in the positive direction — i.e., the flux produced by the control winding aids that produced by the feedback winding — the total core flux is increased, and consequently the reactor impedance decreases. As a result, a larger load current flows, and the load output voltage increases. This condition continues until core saturation is reached.

As the control current is increased in a negative direction, the control winding flux opposes that of the feedback winding. Therefore, the reactor impedance will prevail until the point is reached at which the control flux is equal and opposite to that of the feedback winding [point A in Fig. 8-1(a)]. Beyond this point, further increases in control current produce a flux that overrides the feedback flux, so that the reactor impedance commences to decrease, and load current increases, slowly.

The slope of the section of curve between points A and B in Fig. 8-1(a) is determined by the percentage of feedback. As the feedback is increased, the slope increases so that the load current for a given change in control current varies more for a regenerative amplifier than for a non-feedback one. Actually both circuits, feedback and non-feedback, require the same total core flux fluctuation to produce a given effect; however the flux is produced solely by the direct control current in the non-regenerative amplifier, but is produced jointly by the control current and the feedback current in the regenerative amplifier. Thus, in the latter case, a smaller amount of direct control current is required to produce the same effect as that of a larger control current in the non-feedback case. As the feedback is increased above 100 per cent, snap-action (described in Art. 8-8) occurs. To maintain good stability, the feedback factor is usually kept below 0.85.

It should be obvious, at this point, that one major difference between feedback in conventional electronic amplifiers and that in magnetic amplifiers lies in the effect of the control circuit on the effective input impedance. In the magnetic amplifier, the feedback current component flows in the external feedback windings and the feedback effects are produced by the inductive coupling existing between the associated windings. As a result, the impedance of the control circuit is determined only by the resistance comprising the actual resistance of the control windings and any series resistance (the latter included to increase the speed of response of the magnetic amplifier since the time constant t for an inductive circuit is L in henries/R in ohms). It will be remembered, however, that in the conventional electronic amplifier, the actual magnitude of the input circuit impedance is determined by the feedback.

8-4. Elementary external feedback circuit

The fundamental saturable reactor is equipped with two windings; one is the load and the other the control winding. For purposes of external magnetic feedback, a third winding, the feedback winding N_F, is added to the reactor (Fig. 8-2). To produce a regenerative effect, the flux produced by this winding must aid that produced by the control winding. For degeneration, the fluxes must oppose.

Figure 8-3 illustrates a fundamental regenerative feedback amplifier capable of operating into an a-c load. To follow the circuit operation, assume that the a-c supply is on the half-cycle having the circled polarity. Electrons flow from the negative end of the supply through rectifier SR_1, feedback winding N_F of reactor SX_1, the series-connected load windings N_L of both reactors, and the load R_L back to the supply. On the next half-cycle, electrons flow through the load R_L, both load windings N_L, the feedback winding N_F of reactor SX_2, and rectifier SR_2, completing the path back to the supply. The electron flow direction through the feedback windings is always the same regardless of the supply half-cycle, so that the flux produced around the windings always has the same polarity.

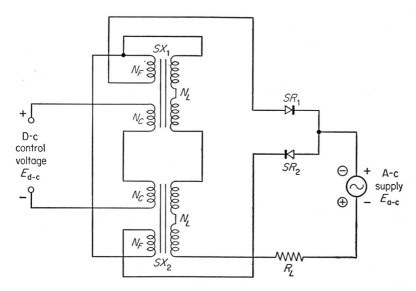

Fig. 8-3. Magnetic amplifier with external regenerative magnetic feedback, operating into a-c load.

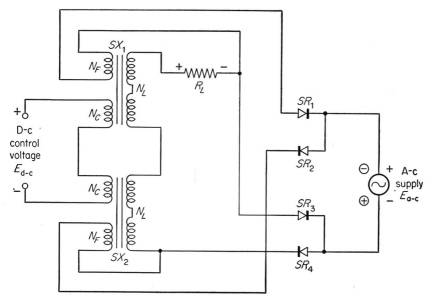

Fig. 8-4. Magnetic amplifier with external regenerative magnetic feedback, operating into d-c load.

In order to have the regenerative effect, the flux produced by the control windings must be aided by that produced by the feedback windings. The fluxes will aid, producing positive feedback, when the d-c control voltage has the indicated polarity. (If the control voltage polarity is reversed, degeneration occurs.) This amplifier operates into an a-c load R_L. This can be seen since the electron flow through the load changes direction on alternate half-cycles.

Figure 8-4 illustrates a second fundamental regenerative amplifier. This amplifier, unlike the one shown in Fig. 8-3, operates into a d-c load. When the a-c has the circled polarity, electrons flow through rectifier SR_1, feedback winding N_F of reactor SX_1, the load R_L, the series-connected load windings N_L of both reactors, and rectifier SR_4 completing the path. On the next half-cycle, rectifiers SR_2 and SR_3 are conductive; electrons flow through SR_3, R_L, both N_L windings, N_F of SX_2, and SR_2. On both half-cycles, the voltage developed across the load has the same d-c polarity. As in the circuit shown in Fig. 8-3, the fluxes produced around the control and feedback windings aid each other when the d-c control voltage has the indicated polarity.

Figure 8-5 shows another regenerative magnetic amplifier capable of driving a d-c load. This circuit differs from the others described

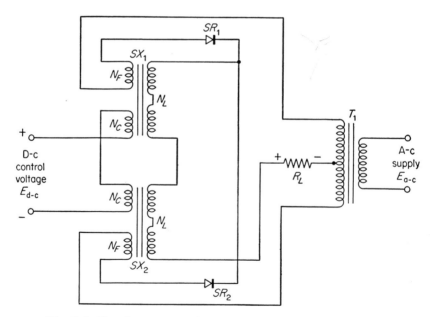

Fig. 8-5. Transformer-operated magnetic amplifier with external regenerative magnetic feedback, operating into d-c load.

here primarily in that it is transformer-operated. The center-tapped secondary of transformer T_1 supplies a-c voltage to the magnetic amplifier.

The regenerative magnetic amplifiers of Figs. 8-3, 8-4, and 8-5 operate into either a-c or d-c loads, but not both simultaneously. If it is necessary to drive a-c and d-c loads at the same time, the circuit

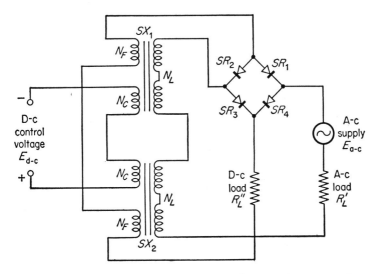

Fig. 8-6. Magnetic amplifier with external magnetic regenerative feedback, capable of operating into a-c and d-c loads simultaneously.

shown in Fig. 8-6 may be used. A d-c control voltage of indicated polarity is connected to the series-aiding control windings N_C. The a-c supply voltage is applied to the load windings N_L and to a bridge rectifier, and a rectified voltage appears across the feedback windings N_F.

To follow the circuit operation, assume that the upper end of the a-c supply shown in this figure is negative. On this half-cycle, electrons flow through rectifier SR_1, the series-connected windings N_F of saturable reactors SX_1 and SX_2, d-c load R_L'', rectifier SR_3 and the series-connected windings N_L of both reactors, and through the a-c load R_L' back to the source. On the next half-cycle, electrons flow through the loads and the load windings in the opposite direction, through rectifier SR_2, through the feedback windings in the same direction as during the preceding half-cycle, and through rectifier SR_4 to the source. Thus although the voltage across the load R_L' and the load windings N_L is a-c, both the voltage applied to the feedback windings N_F and the current flowing through the windings and the d-c load R''_L are unidirectional.

When the d-c control voltage is of the polarity indicated in Fig. 8-6, the flux produced by the control windings is the same as that produced by the feedback windings, and the feedback is positive or regenerative. Basically, then, the rectified load current aids the magnetic flux of the control windings, thereby permitting these windings to have a much larger control effect than they would without feedback. The feedback windings set up an added, and aiding, magnetomotive force in the core, the magnitude of which is proportional to the feedback current representing the rectified load current.

The output voltage waveforms appearing across the a-c load resistance R'_L and the d-c load resistance R''_L vary depending upon the polarity as well as the amplitude of the d-c control voltage. (Positive control voltage polarity is as illustrated in Fig. 8-6.) The waveforms reflect the fact that the impedances of both reactors increase or decrease simultaneously, as noted by the fact that the waveform amplitudes on successive half-cycles are equal.

Because of the flux variations around the load windings, voltage variations are induced from them into the control windings. However, the circuit arrangement is such that the fundamental and odd harmonics induced into one control winding cancel those induced into the other. This cancellation occurs regardless of whether or not control voltage is applied.

A magnetic amplifier circuit using parallel-connected a-c load windings is shown in Fig. 8-7. The basic operation of this circuit is similar to that described for Fig. 8-6, inasmuch as the current through the load resistor R_L and the load windings N_L is alternating, whereas the feedback current through the windings N_F is unidirectional. The flux produced by control windings is aided by the flux around the feedback windings. Because of the parallel load windings, the load current splits equally between these windings.

One of the primary differences between series- and parallel-connected feedback amplifiers lies in the time response of the unit to fluctuations in the d-c control voltage. If, for example, the control voltage is increased suddenly, a transient current is induced into the load windings of the circuit. The transient induced into the parallel-connected load windings of Fig. 8-7 flows in this closed loop formed by these windings, and sets up a flux opposing the control flux. As a result, the parallel-connected circuit shows an increased time of response by responding more slowly to control signals.

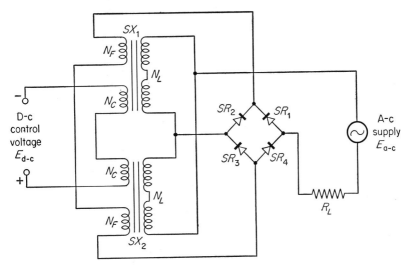

Fig. 8-7. Magnetic amplifier with regenerative external feedback, load windings connected in parallel.

The addition of regenerative feedback in magnetic amplifier circuits reduces the necessary input control power, and increases the power gain. If, however, too much positive feedback is introduced, an infinitesimally small control voltage will trigger a large change in load current. The instability produced as a result of the feedback is referred to as *snap action*. When the magnetic amplifier is used for certain relaying operations, this action is highly desirable. (See Art. 8-8.) When, however, smooth and steady control is required, the snap action is undesirable.

8-5. Introduction of bias into external-feedback amplifier

In an ideal external-feedback magnetic amplifier, the load current would be zero when the control current was zero. This is not true in practice; as shown in Fig. 8-8(a), a certain quiescent load current is present even when $I_C = 0.$* Whereas this quiescent current might

---

* The actual value of quiescent load current is determined by the physical dimensions and electrical characteristics of the reactors, by the amplitude and frequency of the supply voltage, and by the turns ratio between the feedback and load windings.

be considered as a negligible factor in the analysis of a non-feedback circuit, it can hardly be considered in this manner in a regenerative circuit since the feedback will necessarily produce sizable circuit

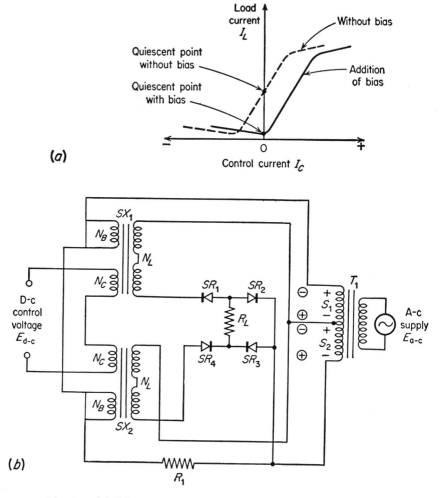

Fig. 8-8. (a) Effect on characteristic curve of adding bias to magnetic amplifier. (b) Matched-impedance a-c bias circuit for reducing quiescent current (feedback circuits not shown).

effects. Accordingly, steps are taken to minimize the quiescent current and its effects, normally by means of a bias circuit. Basically, the bias is used to produce a magnetic core flux which is in opposition to the flux produced by the quiescent current flowing in the feedback windings. The effect of this is to desaturate the core and shift the characteristic curve to the right, as illustrated in Fig. 8-8(a). The application of bias does not affect the shape of the characteristic curve. In a typical unbiased feedback amplifier, the quiescent current might be as high as 50 milliamperes. The application of bias can reduce this to approximately 1 milliampere or less.

Although the bias used for this purpose is normally d-c, a-c bias circuits are sometimes encountered. An advantage of a-c biasing is that bias rectifiers are not required for circuit operation. In Fig. 8-8(b), an a-c bias circuit (also called matched-impedance bias) is used for the reduction of the quiescent current. (For circuit simplification, the conventional feedback windings are not shown in this illustration.) The a-c supply voltage is applied to the primary of transformer T_1, and appears across the tapped secondary windings, labeled S_1 and S_2 for convenience. On the half-cycle when the transformer has the circled polarity, electrons flow from the top end of S_1 through the bias windings N_B of both reactors and through resistor R_1 to the positive end of the transformer. The potential across S_2 forces electrons through load winding N_L of reactor SX_1, rectifier SR_1, load R_L, and rectifier SR_3 to the positive potential end of S_2. On the next half-cycle, this polarity reverses, but the basic action remains the same. As a result, the magnetization produced by the bias windings is such that, regardless of the half-cycle under discussion, it opposes the magnetization of the load windings, and reduces the quiescent current to the desired minimum value.

8-6. Push-pull external-feedback magnetic amplifier

As indicated earlier, certain control applications require the use of a magnetic amplifier, the output of which can be reduced to zero or changed in direction. An amplifier of this type must have the duo-directional transfer characteristics of Fig. 6-11(a). They can be obtained by using two saturable reactors of identical characteristics in a balanced arrangement as described in Chapter 6, or, in the event that high efficiency is required and the limitations of conventional push-pull circuits must be overcome, by using four reactors connected in a symmetrical bridge circuit.

However, two saturable reactors connected in a push-pull circuit can provide satisfactory results provided that regenerative external feedback is used. A push-pull circuit of this variety using external regenerative feedback is illustrated in Fig. 8-9. A cursory examination of this circuit might lead to the conclusion that it is identical to the one shown in Fig. 8-6. This is not true, of course; the reactors of the push-pull circuit of Fig. 8-9 have their load and control windings con-

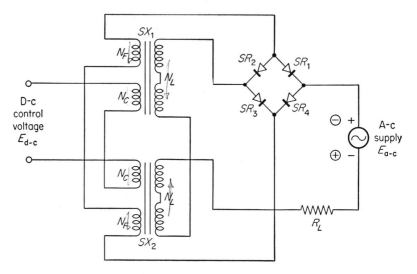

Fig. 8-9. Push-pull magnetic amplifier with external magnetic regenerative feedback.

nected in such a manner that push-pull action is obtained. If, for example, the circuit is examined during the half-cycle when the a-c supply voltage has the circled polarity, and the d-c control voltage is at zero value, the following conditions derive: in saturable reactor SX_2, the flux produced by the load winding N_L opposes that produced by the feedback winding N_F; in saturable reactor SX_1, the flux produced by the load winding N_L aids that of feedback winding N_F. Under these circumstances, the impedance of reactor SX_2 is large, and that of SX_1 low.

When on the next half-cycle the supply voltage changes polarity, the fluxes of the load and feedback windings of SX_2 are additive, so that the impedance of this reactor is low, while the flux of the load windings of SX_1 opposes that of the feedback winding, and the SX_1 impedance is high.

In the absence of control voltage (which may be either d-c or a-c) the total impedance of the two load windings does not change from half-cycle to half-cycle, so that the load voltage waveform and magnitude remain fixed. When a positive control voltage is applied, i.e., when the control voltage of Fig. 8-9 has the circled polarity, the fluxes produced by the dual control windings have unequal effects on alternate half-cycles. The total reactor impedance is high during the first half-cycle so that the output voltage is low, and this condition reverses during the next half-cycle.

In the a-c controlled push-pull amplifier, as in the d-c controlled non-push-pull circuit, the flux variations around the load windings induce voltages into the control windings. However, in the former case the fundamental and odd harmonics are canceled in the control windings only when the a-c control voltage is at zero. At all other times, harmonics of large magnitude appear in the control windings.

Another form of the two-reactor push-pull magnetic amplifier is illustrated in Fig. 8-10. (The feedback windings have been omitted for

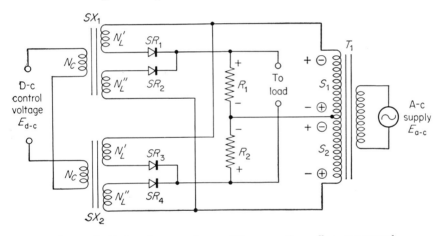

Fig. 8-10. Push-pull magnetic amplifier operating off center-tapped power transformer (feedback circuits not shown).

circuit simplification.) The a-c supply voltage is applied to the primary of transformer T_1 and appears across the secondary windings S_1 and S_2. On the half-cycle when the secondary potential is of the circled polarity, electrons flow from the center-tap through resistor R_2, rectifier SR_4, and load winding N_L'' of reactor SX_2, completing the circuit. At the same time, electrons flow from the center-tap through resistor R_1, rectifier SR_2, and load winding N_L'' of reactor SX_1, completing the circuit. On this half-cycle, the fluxes produced around both load windings N_L'' are of such direction that one flux will aid one of the control winding fluxes while the other opposes the second control winding flux. On the next half-cycle, the opposite conditions prevail, such that rectifier SR_1 and SR_3 are conductive, and flux is produced around both N'_L windings. Now the opposite control winding fluxes are aided and opposed. As a result, push-pull action is obtained.

8-7. Four-reactor push-pull magnetic amplifier

Although the two-reactor magnetic amplifiers described in the preceding article provide highly satisfactory results in certain applications, it is found that their stability is not completely independent of changes in the power-supply voltage and ambient temperature. This shortcoming becomes more evident when the two reactors are not matched, that is, when their characteristics are not identical. For proper match, the quiescent current of both magnetic amplifiers must be zero when the control voltage is zero, and further, their characteristics must agree over the operating range to the units.

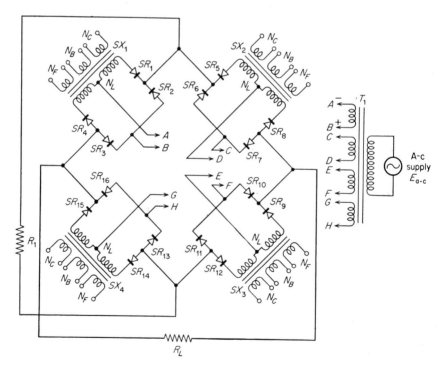

Fig. 8-11. Four-reactor bridge push-pull magnetic amplifier.

When this limitation of the two-reactor must be overcome, four-core push-pull magnetic amplifiers can be used with excellent results. A bridge circuit of this type is illustrated in Fig. 8-11. The load R_L represents any conventional a-c load. Each of the four reactors has a load winding N_L, a feedback winding N_F, a control winding N_C, and a bias winding N_B, although only the load windings are shown connected to simplify the diagram. The supply voltage is taken from four identical secondary windings on a power transformer.

In this bridge circuit, reactors SX_1 and SX_3 work together, as do reactors SX_2 and SX_4. To follow the operation, assume that the supply half-cycle is such as to produce the indicated polarity at winding AB. Electrons flow through a portion of the N_L winding of reactor SX_1, rectifier SR_4, load R_L, rectifier SR_9, the N_L winding of SX_3, rectifier SR_{12}, resistor R_1, and rectifier SR_2, completing the circuit. Similar action occurs for the other reactors, and push-pull action results.

The bias windings are connected so that the amplifiers are operating with no quiescent load current. The control windings are connected so as to produce push-pull action. The feedback windings are connected to give a regenerative effect. When d-c control voltage of either polarity is applied, the impedance of SX_1-SX_3 increases and that of SX_3-SX_4 decreases, or vice versa. As a result, a load component appears, the magnitude of which is determined both by the degree of unbalance produced by the control current, and by the individual transfer characteristics of the reactors.

8-8. Regenerative feedback snap action

Snap action, as mentioned in Art. 8-3, results when excessive positive feedback is introduced into a circuit, thereby producing circuit instability. In certain relay applications, snap action is both required and desirable. In the case of relay operation, changing the relay current from a small value below relay pick-up to a large value considerably above pick-up produces rapid and certain contact action. Conversely, when de-energizing the relay, changing the coil current from a large value to one well below pick-up extends the life of the contacts by minimizing the tendency of the contacts to arc. Furthermore, under these conditions shock and vibration effects are less noticed.

A circuit that utilizes snap action to produce an efficiently operating relay is shown in Fig. 8-12. The a-c supply voltage is applied to the primary of a transformer, the secondary of which has center-tapped

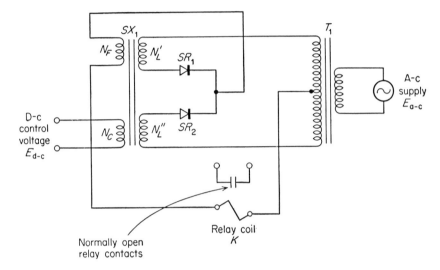

Fig. 8-12. Relay operation resulting from snap action.

windings. The secondary voltage is applied to the parallel circuits comprising the load windings N'_L and N''_L and the rectifiers SR_1 and SR_2. Because of the rectifiers, direct current flows through the relay coil winding and the positive feedback winding N_F of the saturable reactor. In the absence of control voltage, the feedback current and its corresponding magnetic flux are relatively low because of the impedance of the load windings. Thus, the relay current is not sufficient for pick-up. When control voltage of a certain amplitude is applied, the load windings impedance decreases, and the increase in feedback current causes snap action to occur, actuating the relay.

8-9. A-c controlled feedback

In the feedback magnetic amplifiers described up to this point the feedback current, obtained through rectification, flowed in the feedback windings N_F, which were independent of the control windings N_C. Furthermore, the control current was d-c in nature. This arrangement is not the only possible solution for control in an external-feedback magnetic amplifier. Actually, the circuit can be controlled by means of an a-c, rather than d-c, voltage. A circuit permitting this type of control is shown in Fig. 8-13.

On the half-cycle when the a-c supply voltage has the circled polarity, current flows through the feedback windings N_F and the load

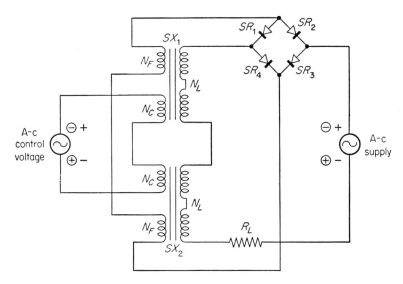

Fig. 8-13. A-c control of a regenerative magnetic amplifier.

windings N_L in series with load resistor R_L. On the half-cycle when the a-c control voltage has the circled polarity, current flows in the series-connected control windings N_C. If the two a-c voltages are directly in phase, the fluxes produced by the feedback windings add to that of the control windings, and the impedance of the reactors is at its minimum. Consequently the voltage developed across the load is at its maximum.

It is not necessary for control purposes that the control voltage and the source voltage remain in phase. In actuality, varying the phase of the control voltage with respect to the supply voltage is one method of controlling the output of the magnetic amplifier. In another case, a resistor in series with the control windings is made variable so that the control voltage amplitude is adjustable, while the phase relationship between the two a-c voltages is held constant; i.e., the phase is adjusted to the value that produces the optimum operating conditions for the circuit under control.

REVIEW QUESTIONS

1. The feedback factor for a regenerative magnetic amplifier is $1 - N_F/N_L$, as shown in Eq. (8-2b). For a degenerative amplifier, this factor becomes $1 + N_F/N_L$. Discuss the current gain of a degenerative magnetic amplifier for: (a) $N_F < N_L$; (b) $N_F = N_L$; and (c) $N_F > N_L$.

2. A magnetic amplifier has 2000 turns in the control winding, 500 turns in the load winding, and 200 turns in the regenerative feedback winding. If the resistance of the load circuit is 10,000 ohms and that of the control circuit is 100 ohms, what is the power gain of the amplifier?

3. Three magnetic amplifiers are connected in cascade. The first amplifier has a power gain of 75 and a response speed of 12 cps; the second amplifier has a gain of 50 and a response speed of 10 cps; the third amplifier has a gain of 60 and a response speed of 8 cps. What is the over-all figure of merit?

4. Is the voltage developed across R_L in Fig. 8-8(b) a-c or d-c?

The Magnetic Amplifier with Internal Feedback

9-1. Introduction

As explained in Chapter 8, external feedback in a magnetic amplifier is generally accomplished by means of additional auxiliary windings, whereas internal (intrinsic) feedback occurs without the addition of special windings. A magnetic amplifier that uses internal feedback is sometimes referred to as a *self-saturating* or *auto-excited circuit*, for reasons that become obvious later in this chapter. Self-saturation in a magnetic amplifier is accomplished by connecting rectifying components in series with the load windings of the saturable reactor. A comparison of the operational characteristics of internal- and external-feedback amplifiers reveals that there is little difference between the two types. However, the self-saturating amplifier has the advantage that a simpler reactor is required (one with no feedback windings). This is important not only because it simplifies the construction of the magnetic amplifier but also because it eliminates the resistance of the external feedback windings (through which the load current must flow). Another advantage of the self-saturating circuit is that the lack of a feedback winding allows the load winding to be wound over a greater area of the reactor frame, and this, for a frame of given size, permits a greater power output than in the case of the external-feedback amplifier. It should be noted, however, that the external-feedback amplifier is sometimes desired because its gain can be adjusted easily.

In certain applications it is desirable to combine, in one circuit, the effects produced by external and internal feedbacks operating simultaneously to increase the amplifier gains further. Devices of this nature are termed compound feedback circuits.

A few of the more important circuit applications of self-saturating magnetic amplifiers are in:

1. Voltage and speed regulating circuits.
2. Telemetering devices for remotely controlled aircraft or remotely controlled industrial systems.
3. Servomechanisms.
4. Thermocouple and photoelectric circuits.
5. Hydraulic servo control systems.
6. Computer circuits.

9-2. The basic internal-feedback magnetic amplifier

In the basic internal-feedback circuit, a rectifier is connected in series with the a-c supply voltage and the load windings of the saturable reactor, so that only a unidirectional, pulsating current is permitted to flow in these windings. As a result, the core flux level never decreases below a specific minimum value, which is determined necessarily by the a-c supply voltage, the load current, and the magnetic core flux produced by the control voltage. Basically, a direct-current component proportional to the mean value of the alternating load current flows through the load windings. In effect, this component acts to produce the internal feedback.

A fundamental half-wave internal-feedback circuit is illustrated in Fig. 9-1. Note that no external feedback windings are included on the reactor. In this circuit, the a-c supply voltage is rectified by rectifier SR_1, so that unidirectional current flows in the load windings only during one half-cycle of the applied voltage. The direction of this component and that of the flux it produces are always the same, and are not dependent upon the control current. Control current flows in the control windings as determined by the magnitude of the control voltage and the setting of potentiometer R. (Although d-c control is indicated in Fig. 9-1, a-c control is also applicable.)

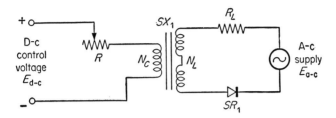

Fig. 9-1. Basic internal-feedback (self-saturating) magnetic amplifier.

During the half-cycle when load current flows, the core flux magnetization is produced by the flux around the load winding plus that around the control winding. In the illustrated circuit and during the half-cycle with the indicated control-voltage polarity, the core approaches saturation, and the reactor impedance decreases. As a result the load current is high, and the load voltage $I_L R_L$ is correspondingly large. On the next half-cycle, no voltage appears across the load winding. The value of flux density is determined solely by the current through the control winding.

The impedance of the reactor and the consequent load current and voltage waveform are all determined by the value of control voltage. When it is large the initial flux density is set to a relatively high level during that half-cycle when the rectifier is nonconducting. In the next half-cycle, a pulsating load current flows in the a-c windings, bringing the core toward saturation. As a result, the reactor impedance is decreased.

In the absence of control current, the rectified load current will produce a large core flux, lowering the reactance of the device, in turn leading to a sizable amount of quiescent load current I_Q. The value of I_Q is affected by the physical dimensions and electrical characteristics of the core and by the frequency and amplitude of the a-c supply voltage. The quiescent current may be decreased, as usual, by the application of bias, as described later in this chapter.

In the circuit of Fig. 9-1, the control voltage polarity and the control winding direction are such that the feedback flux produced by the load winding is in phase with that of the control winding. If, however, the control voltage polarity is reversed, or the control winding is wound oppositely, the fluxes produced will oppose. In this case, an increase in control voltage will bring the core away from its saturation level, and the reactor impedance will increase. As a result, the load current and voltage output will decrease. Thus, the basic internal-feedback circuit of Fig. 9-1 may be considered as a polarized device, able to distinguish between positive and negative control voltages.

9-3. Two-reactor internal-feedback amplifier

A basic two-reactor self-saturating magnetic amplifier is illustrated in Fig. 9-2. In this circuit, control is maintained by means of a d-c voltage. Now, assume that the polarity of the a-c supply voltage is as circled. On this half-cycle, electrons flow through rectifier SR_2, the load winding N_L of reactor SX_2, and the load R_L. On the next half-

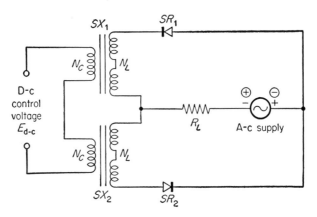

Fig. 9-2. Two-reactor doubler internal-feedback magnetic amplifier.

cycle, electrons flow through the load in the opposite direction, and through load winding N_L of reactor SX_1 and rectifier SR_1. From the circuit operation described thus far, it is obvious that rectified half-wave pulses of current flow in each of the reactor load windings, so that internal feedback is produced by means of the d-c component of the pulses. Furthermore, it is clear that the voltage appearing across the load resistance R_L is a-c in nature.

The polarity and magnitude of the d-c control voltage will, of course, determine the amplitude of the a-c voltage developed across the load. With d-c voltage of one polarity, the core flux produced by the control voltage will aid the flux generated around the load windings. Under this set of conditions, the impedances of the reactors are low, and the subsequent voltage across the load is high. Increasing the magnitude of the control voltage while maintaining this selfsame polarity will cause the load voltage to increase further, until core saturation is reached, at which point the load voltage can increase no more.

When the control-voltage polarity is reversed, the control core fluxes oppose those produced by the load windings. As a result, the impedances of the reactors are high, and the load voltage is low. As the magnitude of the control voltage is increased, the load voltage decreases. However, as the control voltage is increased, a point will be reached at which the control flux equals the load flux; at this point, the reactor impedance will be at its maximum, and the load voltage at minimum. As the control voltage is increased further, the control flux will be greater than the load flux, and the load voltage will increase slowly.

The conditions may be observed in the transfer characteristics of the feedback circuit, Fig. 8-1. Note that for positive values of control current (the control flux aiding the load flux), the load current rises to saturation. For negative values of control current (the control flux opposing the load flux), the load current decreases to a minimum, and then starts to rise slowly. Note also that a definite quiescent current, i.e., the value of I_L when I_c is zero, can be observed on the curve.

The two-reactor magnetic amplifier may be a-c as well as d-c controlled. The control operation is the same as that described for the a-c controlled external-feedback amplifier. The a-c control voltage has the same frequency as the a-c supply voltage.

The doubler circuit of Fig. 9-2 operates into an a-c load; it supplies an a-c output of the same frequency as the supply voltage. The amplifier of Fig. 9-3, while basically the same type of circuit, is a

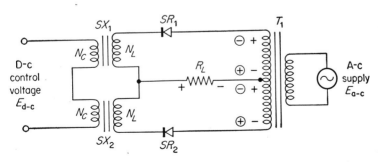

Fig. 9-3. Two-reactor full-wave internal-feedback magnetic amplifier.

full-wave device which operates into a d-c load; the load current contains two pulses for each cycle of the supply voltage.

A transformer with a center-tapped secondary winding is used to provide the a-c supply in the amplifier of Fig. 9-3. When the secondary voltage has the circled polarity (Fig. 9-3), the a-c voltage across the lower portion of the secondary is rectified by rectifier SR_2, and voltage of the indicated polarity appears across the load resistance R_L. On the next half-cycle, the potential across the upper half of the secondary is rectified by SR_1, and voltage of the selfsame polarity is developed across the load. The pulsating current flowing through the load windings on the alternating half-cycles contains the d-c component required for internal feedback. The amplitude of the control voltage determines the load current that flows in both reactors, and consequently the d-c output voltage.

The amplifier illustrated in Fig. 9-4 is another form of full-wave circuit. Because of its bridge connection, however, it does not require

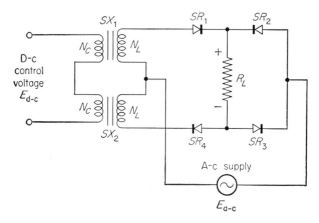

Fig. 9-4. Two-reactor single-phase full-wave bridge magnetic amplifier.

a center-tapped supply, as did the full-wave circuit of Fig. 9-3. In the bridge circuit, electron flow is through rectifiers SR_1 and SR_3 on one half-cycle of the a-c supply, and through SR_2 and SR_4 on the next half-cycle. The load voltage has the polarity shown in Fig. 9-4.

The performance characteristics of the full-wave circuits of Figs. 9-3 and 9-4 are almost the same when operating into a resistive load, but they vary radically when the load is inductive. From Fig. 9-3 it can be noted that, if the load were inductive, any counter emf built up across the load would discharge through a path containing the load windings of a reactor. As a result, the additional core flux produced makes the amplifier exhibit unstable characteristics. In the bridge circuit of Fig. 9-4, however, any counter emf built up across an inductive load can find a discharge path other than through the load windings. As a result, the bridge circuit has performance characteristics which are more easily predicted, and which have greater stability.

9-4. Two-reactor push-pull internal-feedback magnetic amplifier

Figure 9-5 illustrates a basic half-wave push-pull amplifier, which consists of identical saturable reactors SX_1 and SX_2, and associated rectifiers SR_1 and SR_2. The circuit is considered as half-wave inasmuch as both rectifiers conduct during the same half-cycle, so that

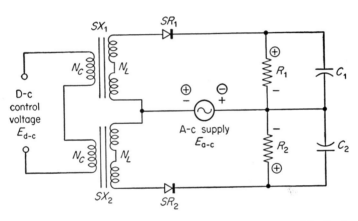

Fig. 9-5. Half-wave push-pull magnetic amplifier with internal feedback.

load current flows simultaneously in the load windings of the reactors. The output voltage is the sum of the potentials across the two load resistors R_1 and R_2. Note that these potentials are of opposite polarity. Consequently, the resultant output voltage (the voltage across both resistors) will be positive or negative, depending upon the control voltage polarity, and will be zero in the absence of control voltage.

On the half-cycle when the supply voltage has the circled polarity, electrons flow from the negative end of the supply through resistor R_1, the N_L winding of reactor SX_1 and rectifier SR_1, to the positive end of the supply. Simultaneously, current flows from the negative end of the supply through R_2, the N_L winding of SX_2, and SR_2 back to the source. The voltages developed across the resistors have the indicated polarities. On the next half-cycle, no rectifier conduction occurs, which is to be expected as this device is a half-wave magnetic amplifier. Filter capacitors are connected across the resistors to decrease the output ripple.

As indicated, the control voltage polarity is important in the determination of the polarity of the output, and the control voltage magnitude is important in the determination of the output amplitude. The control windings are so connected that the core flux produced by one will aid the flux around one load winding, while the flux produced by the other opposes the flux of its associated load winding. Thus the impedance of one reactor increases, while that of the second decreases, and this action reverses on the next half-cycle, so that push-pull action is produced. In this manner, a reversible output is obtained. If, however, the control windings are connected such that the impedances of both reactors increase or decrease simultaneously, then so-called normal or doubler action occurs.

A basic two-reactor full-wave push-pull internal-feedback amplifier which is capable of operating into either a-c or d-c loads is shown in Fig. 9-6. On the half-cycle when the a-c supply voltage has the circled polarity, electrons flow through resistor R_1, rectifier SR_1, the load winding N_L of reactor SX_1, and resistor R_3 to the positive po-

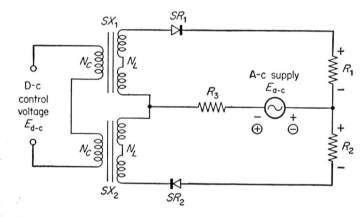

Fig. 9-6. Two-reactor full-wave push-pull magnetic amplifier with internal feedback.

tential end of the source. On the next half-cycle, rectifier SR_1 is non-conductive but rectifier SR_2 conducts, producing a pulsating load current in the N_L winding of SX_2. The potential developed across resistor R_3 is of opposite polarity to that produced on the first half-cycle, and that across R_2 is as indicated in the illustration. Basically, then, full-wave action occurs because the rectifiers permit conduction on alternate half-cycles. In addition, since the rectifiers are in series with the load windings, internal feedback is generated. The voltage developed across resistor R_3 is a-c in nature, so that this resistor can be replaced by an a-c load. The voltage developed across resistor R_1 and R_2 is d-c, so that this circuit can be used to operate a d-c load.

The control voltage can be d-c of either polarity, reversing or steady, or a-c. However, regardless of the control polarity or type, the circuit action is such that the impedances of the two reactors always change in directions opposite to each other. In other words, if the SX_1 impedance increases by a certain amount, the SX_1 impedance will decrease by the same amount, thereby simulating push-pull action. The impedance of a reactor will increase when load and control fluxes oppose each other, and will decrease when the fluxes are additive.

9-5. Biasing the internal-feedback amplifier

It has been mentioned in Art. 9-2 that the load current which flows under no-signal conditions reaches a large value in the internal-feedback magnetic amplifier. As described for the external-feedback magnetic amplifier in Chapter 8, bias voltages, either d-c or a-c, may be applied to the self-saturating amplifier circuit in order to decrease the magnitude of this quiescent current, and thus reduce its effects to a point at which they no longer are objectionable.

9-6. Compound feedback magnetic amplifier

In certain amplifier applications, the total feedback of the circuit is developed by both internal and external means. The internal feedback is introduced normally, by applying a pulsating unidirectional current to the load winding. The external feedback is generated by the use of additional inductively coupled external feedback windings. Applications are noted in which the two feedbacks aid each other, thereby producing a large feedback effect, or oppose each other, in which case the total feedback is reduced.

A typical magnetic amplifier utilizing compound feedback is observed in Fig. 9-7. The load is a-c operated in this particular circuit. To follow the operation, assume that the a-c supply voltage is on the half-cycle having the circled polarity. During this time interval, electrons flow through the load R_L, rectifier SR_6, the feedback windings of N_F of both reactors SX_1 and SX_2, rectifier SR_4, the load winding N_L of reactor SX_1, and rectifier SR_1 to the positive end of the supply voltage. On the next half-cycle, current flows in the load winding N_L of reactor SX_2.

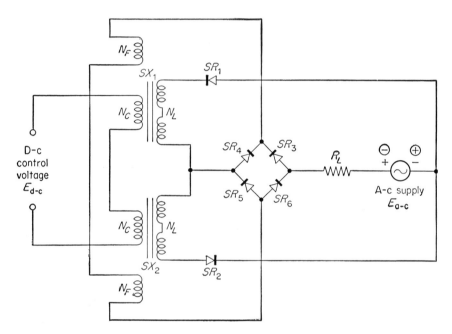

Fig. 9-7. Compound feedback magnetic amplifier, using internal and external feedback.

Analyzing this circuit operation, it can be seen that feedback is effected by allowing unidirectional current to flow in the feedback windings N_F (as determined by bridge rectifiers SR_3, SR_4, SR_5, SR_6, which conduct in pairs) and in the load windings N_L (as permitted by rectifiers SR_1 and SR_2, only one of which conducts at a time). Thus compound feedback is made available. The total feedback so produced is determined by whether the individual feedbacks oppose or aid each other, by the current flowing through the load windings and the number of such windings, and by the current flowing through the feedback windings and the number of such windings. Actual control in the compound feedback circuit is accomplished in the same manner as in any other feedback amplifier.

9-7. Multistage internal-feedback amplifiers

All of the internal-feedback amplifiers described thus far in this chapter have utilized single-core reactors. For the purpose of increased gain, these reactors may be connected in cascade. A two-

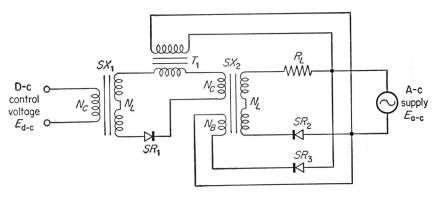

Fig. 9-8. Cascaded magnetic amplifiers, using internal feedback.

stage cascaded circuit comprising magnetic amplifiers with internal feedback is shown in Fig. 9-8. In this circuit arrangement, reactor SX_1 acts as the input stage, the gain of which is controlled by the control (or signal) voltage. This reactor has two windings: the control winding N_C and the load winding N_L. The output stage is built around reactor SX_2, which has three windings: a control winding N_C, a load winding N_L, and a bias winding N_B.

The control voltage sets the core flux density of reactor SX_1, and thereby determines the impedance of this reactor. The a-c supply voltage is applied through transformer T_1 to the secondary circuit comprising the load winding N_L of SX_1, the control winding N_C of SX_2, and rectifier SR_1. Because of the rectifier, current flows in this secondary circuit for one half of the cycle, producing internal feedback in the input stage. The magnitude of current and the effective impedance of reactor SX_2 are determined by the impedance of the SX_1 load winding.

The a-c supply voltage is also applied to the series circuit comprising the load R_L and the half-wave rectifier SR_2. This rectifier insures, of course, that internal feedback is also available for the output stage. The a-c supply, when rectified by SR_3, is also used as a source of bias voltage to reduce the quiescent load current.

9-8. Four-reactor push-pull magnetic amplifier

A four-reactor push-pull magnetic amplifier which uses intrinsic feedback and operates into an a-c load is shown in Fig. 9-9. In this device, four reactors (SX_1 through SX_4) are wired into the circuit, each

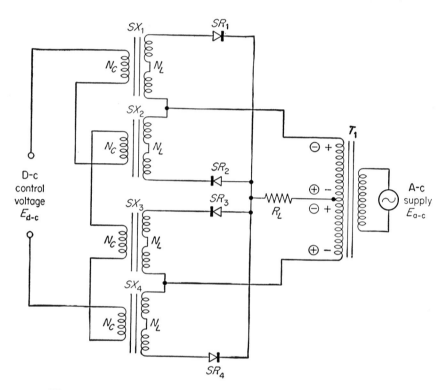

Fig. 9-9. Four-reactor push-pull magnetic amplifier with internal feedback.

reactor having one load and one control winding. Rectifiers SR_1 through SR_4 are connected in series with the load windings so as to produce internal feedback.

If the circuit operation is observed on the half-cycle when the voltage across the center-tapped secondary of transformer T_1 has the circled polarity, electrons will flow from the upper end of the transformer through the load winding N_L of reactor SX_2, rectifier SR_2 and load R_L back to the center-tap. However, electrons will also flow from the center-tap through R_L, rectifier SR_4, and the N_L winding of reactor SX_4 to the lower end of the transformer. In effect, then, no voltage appears across the load at this time since the two load currents are equal but opposite. On the next half-cycle, rectifiers SR_1 and SR_3 are conductive, and flux is produced by the N_L windings of reactors SX_1 and SX_3.

So long as control voltage is absent, the circuit is fully symmetrical and no output voltage appears across the load. However, when control voltage is present, the current through the control windings sets up a core flux which will aid the flux produced by two of the load windings (such as that produced by the N_L windings of SX_1 and SX_2) while opposing the other two (N_L windings of SX_3 and SX_4). As a result, the circuit is asymmetrical, and load voltage appears across R_L.

The circuit of Fig. 9-9 may be considered as the fundamental four-core push-pull internal-feedback circuit. It can be readily modified to operate into a d-c load, to be a-c controlled, or both.

9-9. Three-phase magnetic amplifier

The magnetic amplifiers described to this point have all operated from a single-phase a-c supply. The half-wave amplifier shown in

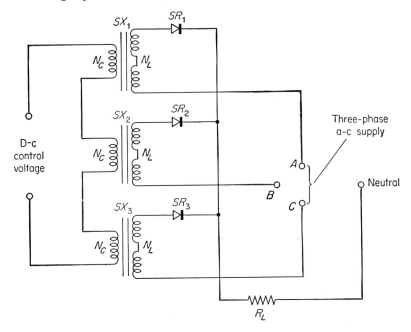

Fig. 9-10. Three-phase half-wave magnetic amplifier with internal feedback.

Fig. 9-10 operates on a three-phase source. Rectifiers SR_1 through SR_3 are connected in series with their respective load windings to produce internal feedback.

Since each of the phases produces the same action, only one need be examined briefly. On that half-cycle when neutral line is negative with respect to point A, electrons flow through load R_L, rectifier SR_1, and the load winding N_L of reactor SX_1. On the next half-cycle, this rectifier is nonconductive. As a result, the voltage across the load is d-c in nature. Because a three-phase supply is being used, the amplitude of the ripple voltage across the load is low.

Figure 9-11 illustrates another three-phase operated amplifier. The bridge arrangement in this circuit permits full-wave push-pull operation. The rectifiers and load windings are connected to conduct in pairs; rectifiers SR_1 and SR_4, SR_2 and SR_5, and SR_3 and SR_6 function together.

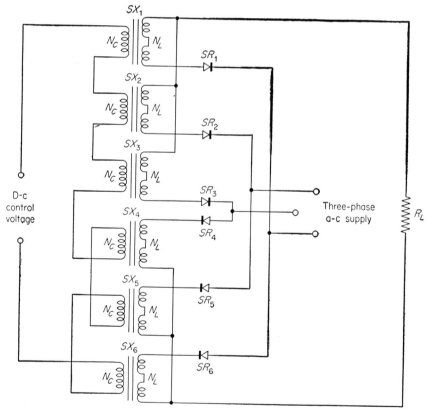

Fig. 9-11. Three-phase bridge full-wave magnetic amplifier.

9-10. Push-pull flux detectors

The flux-gate magnetometer is a device used to measure the effects of external magnetic fields such as, for example, the earth's magnetic field. The magnetometer is essentially a flux-detection unit. A half-wave push-pull circuit used for flux-detection is shown in Fig. 9-12.

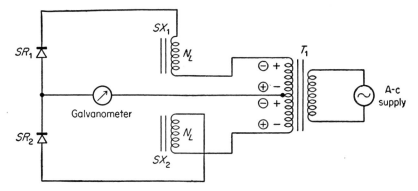

Fig. 9-12. Half-wave internal-feedback magnetic amplifier operating as a magnetometer.

The two equal load windings, which are the pickup coils, are wound on cores of easily saturable magnetic material. The axes of the cores point in the same direction.

To follow the circuit operation, assume first a complete absence of an external magnetic field. On the half-cycle when the a-c supply voltage*has the circled polarity, both rectifiers are conductive, and current flows in the two load windings. However, since the reactors and the rectifiers are identical, no potential difference exists across the ends of the rectifiers and the galvanometer does not register. The fluxes produced in the reactors are of equal magnitude but opposite polarity.

If, now, an external magnetic field is applied, for example, parallel to the axes of the cores, this magnetic field will aid the field produced by one of the reactors while opposing that produced by the other. Because of this, the symmetry of the circuit is destroyed, the impedance of one reactor increases while the other decreases, and the current through one rectifier increases while the other decreases. As a result, differential potential difference exists across the galvanometer. The direction and magnitude of the galvanometer needle deflection is a measure of the direction and strength of the external magnetic field.

---

* The frequency of the supply is usually about 400 cycles per second in this application.

The half-wave push-pull circuit can be adapted easily for use as a position-indicating device. A reactor having a single closed-loop core and two equal load windings is used in this instance, and a permanent magnet, rotatable on a pivot, is mounted in the center of the core. If the permanent magnet were not present to produce an external field, the impedances of the two windings would be equal, and the galvanometer needle would not deflect. In addition, this same condition would prevail if the permanent magnet were so oriented that its flux was perpendicular to the two parallel load windings. If, however, the magnet were rotated (as it may be by being ganged to a mechanical input), the impedance of one reactor would increase while the other would decrease, and galvanometer needle deflection would occur. Thus the physical position of the rotatable magnet can be judged by reference to the needle deflection.

A circuit of this type can be utilized where, because of physical or mechanical design considerations, potentiometers cannot be used. If greater sensitivity is desired the galvanometer can be replaced by the control winding of another magnetic amplifier, and the indicating device can be used as the load into which the amplifier operates.

9-11. Push-pull remote control positioning

Figure 9-13 illustrates a method wherein a push-pull full-wave magnetic amplifier is used for positioning a remote load. The a-c

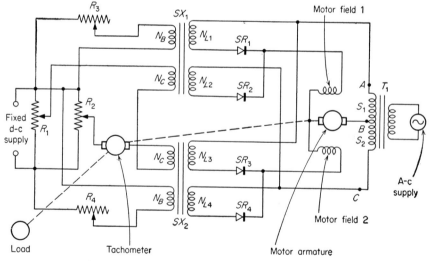

Fig. 9-13. Full-wave remote control positioning circuit.

supply voltage is applied to the primary of transformer T_1; the secondary voltage appears across equal secondary windings S_1 and S_2. On the half-cycle when point B is negative with respect to point A, electrons flow through the motor armature and through parallel paths consisting of motor field winding 1, rectifier SR_1, and load winding N_{L1} (SX_1) in parallel with motor field winding 2, rectifier SR_3, and load winding N_{L3} (SX_2). On the next half-cycle when point B is negative with respect to point C, electrons flow through the motor armature and through parallel paths comprising motor field 1, SR_2, and N_{L2} (SX_1) in parallel with motor field 2, SR_4, and N_{L4} (SX_2). Since the motor has equal but opposite split field windings, the total flux cancels and the motor does not rotate when the load is not being positioned.

When it is desired to position the remote load, the arm of control potentiometer R_1 is moved to a point corresponding to the new desired load location. As a result, a potential difference appears between the arms of control potentiometer R_1 and follow-up potentiometer R_2. Current now flows through the control windings N_C of both saturable reactors.

The magnitude and direction of the fluxes produced by the control windings govern the impedances of the load windings of the reactors; however, the control windings are so arranged that as the impedance of one reactor increases, the impedance of the other decreases. This means, then, that the currents through the split motor fields are no longer equal, and the motor armature begins to rotate in a direction determined by which field flux is larger. As the armature turns and positions the load, it also drives the arm of the follow-up potentiometer R_2 to a position corresponding to that of the control potentiometer R_1. When the arm of R_2 reaches the corresponding position, no potential difference exists between the arms, no current flows in the control windings of the reactors, and the motor field flux returns to zero, stopping the motor.

The tachometer illustrated in the circuit is used to prevent motor hunting or overshooting. To produce this antihunt action, the output of the tachometer, which is proportional to the speed of the motor, is placed in series with the control windings. This tends to regulate the motor speed by holding it within limits (i.e., it does not permit the motor to race), so that the speed is, in effect, proportional to the displacement of the potentiometers.

Two bias windings are included in the circuit, one for each reactor. Potentiometers R_3 and R_4 can be used to adjust the bias levels as required.

REVIEW QUESTIONS

1. Explain why a magnetic amplifier using internal feedback is called a self-saturating circuit.
2. What is the fundamental difference between the self-saturating circuits illustrated in Figs. 9-2 and 9-3?
3. If the load winding of reactor SX_2 becomes defective by opening, will output appear across R_1, R_2, and R_3? Explain your answer.
4. If the control voltage applied to the control winding of reactor SX_1 in Fig. 9-8 is increased, what happens to the voltage developed across R_L?
5. Explain the operation of the circuit of Fig. 9-11. Is the voltage across R_L a-c or d-c? What is an advantage of three-phase operation as compared to single-phase operation?

CHAPTER

10

Magnetic Amplifier
Servomechanism Applications

10-1. Introduction

A servomechanism is a closed-loop (closed-cycle) system consisting of three fundamental circuits; namely, a measurement or comparison circuit for detecting error, an amplifier circuit for increasing its power,

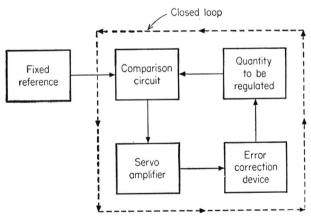

Fig. 10-1. Block diagram of a servomechanism.

173

and an error-correcting circuit, which reduces the error to zero. In a servomechanism system, as shown in Fig. 10-1, the quantity or condition to be regulated is compared with a fixed reference; the difference between the two is considered as the error, and is the signal which is applied to the input of the servo amplifier. The amplifier power output drives a circuit or device in such a manner or direction as to decrease the error to zero, at which time the regulated quantity matches the reference quantity.

The magnetic amplifier lends itself admirably to servo applications. For comparison (or measurement), a current or voltage representing the reference quantity can be applied to a control winding of a magnetic amplifier, and a current or voltage corresponding to the regulated quantity applied to the same winding. By proper choice of circuitry, the fluxes produced by the two quantities can be chosen to be in opposition so that the resultant flux is a measure of the difference between the two quantities. To prevent any unwanted interaction between the two quantities (or between their respective circuits), a magnetic amplifier with two control windings can be used. In this case, the voltage representing the reference quantity is applied to one winding, and that representing the regulated quantity is applied to the other, again in such a manner that the magnetic fluxes so produced buck each other. Because of the characteristics of the magnetic amplifier, complete independence exists between the external circuitry of the quantities applied to the two control windings, thus minimizing problems of electrical isolation and grounding.

The magnetic amplifier itself is also suited to the production of the power output which is used to drive the error-correcting device. It can operate on signal inputs as low as 10^{-10} watt or less, such as are obtained from thermocouples, synchros, phototubes, or the like. If the output device to be actuated has a lower power requirement, as would a relay, for example, a single stage of magnetic amplification is often sufficient. If, however, a larger power must be supplied, cascaded single-ended or push-pull amplifiers can be used to meet the power demands.

Figure 10-2 illustrates how magnetic amplifiers may be applied to servomechanisms. The comparison amplifier has two control windings; the reference voltage is applied to one winding and the voltage representing the quantity under regulation is applied to the other. The output of the comparison amplifier, controlled by the resultant flux of the two control windings, is taken from the load winding of the

comparison amplifier and is applied to the input control winding of
the power amplifier. The output of this amplifier drives the error-

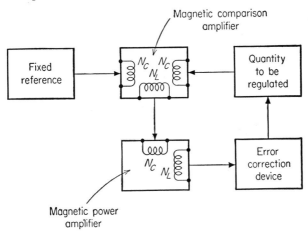

Fig. 10-2. Application of magnetic amplifiers in a servomechanism.

correcting device (a servo motor, for example) in such a direction as to
match the regulated quantity to the reference quantity.

The over-all speed of response of the servomechanism employing
magnetic amplifiers may or may not be of prime importance, depending only upon the particular servo application. If the time of response
of the element producing the quantity to be regulated is high (as it
would be in the case of a thermocouple), then a time lag in the magnetic amplifier corresponding to a few cycles of a-c supply frequency
would not have a significant effect on the operation of the system.
Thus, in speed or temperature control systems, the magnetic amplifier
has found wide use. If, however, the servo response must be rapid, as
in the case of certain automatic control applications, then the time lag
introduced by the magnetic amplifier may become a serious handicap.

10-2. Medium-power positioning servo system

Figure 10-3(a) illustrates the application of the magnetic amplifier
to a medium-power positioning servo system. In this system, a push-
pull magnetic amplifier [Fig. 10-3(b)] is used to control a two-phase
induction servo motor which is capable of delivering 200 watts to the
load shaft. In this and other similar systems, a controlled shaft
delivers much more power than the controlling shaft, and the over-all
action of the device is regulated by an error in angular position as

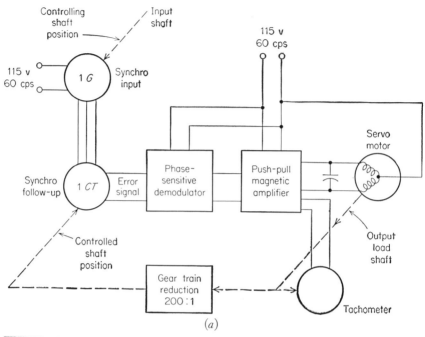

Fig. 10-3. (a) Medium-power positioning servo system. (*After Magnetic Amplifiers, Inc.*) (b) Push-pull magnetic amplifier used in servo application. (*Courtesy, Magnetic Amplifiers, Inc.*)

determined by a comparison between the two shafts. Systems of this type have been used in antenna training systems, stable platform drives, and machine tool controls.

As indicated for this application, the follow-up synchro (control transformer) is used to effect the comparison between the output and input shaft positions. The output of the synchro is an a-c error signal, the magnitude of which is proportional to the angular displacement between the two shaft positions, and the phase angle of which is 0 or 180 degrees with reference to the a-c supply as determined by the direction of the displacement.

The error signal is fed to a phase-sensitive demodulator,* which produces a d-c output proportional to the magnitude of the error, and with a polarity determined by its phase. The demodulator output drives a push-pull magnetic amplifier that supplies a phase-reversible voltage to the control windings of the servo motor. Thus, the load shaft is driven to a position corresponding to the input shaft position.

The d-c permanent-magnet tachometer coupled to the motor produces a signal proportional to the speed of the output shaft. This signal is fed to an input winding of the magnetic amplifier to damp the system for stable operation.

The performance specifications of this typical medium-power positioning servo system, which causes one shaft to follow another in angular motion and which amplifies the torque and power between the two, may be given as follows:

Output power.............	650 watts
Input supply..............	115 volts, 60 cps, single phase
Stabilization..............	Rate feedback from tachometer
Motor...................	Low-inertia, two-phase servo motor. Mechanical power output: 200 watts
Synchro input.............	1 G
Synchro follow-up.........	1 CT
Motor-to-synchro gear ratio..	200
Static accuracy............	1 degree (1 volt rms)
Velocity constant..........	80 degrees per second per degree

10-3. Low-power instrument servo system

One of the most common applications of magnetic amplifiers is in a positional or velocity servo system, similar to that described in the

---

* The phase-sensitive demodulator or detector operates on a phase-reversing a-c signal such as is obtainable from a synchro or a variable transformer. At zero signal conditions, no output is obtained.

preceding paragraph. In this system, used for instrumentation, the servo drives a load having a mechanical power requirement in the order of a few watts or less. In many applications, the load inertial and friction constants are such as to present a negligible drag to the motor rotor, so that, for all practical purposes, the motor is running free.

Figure 10-4 shows a block diagram of a typical positional loop, and Fig. 10-5 illustrates the system connections of the circuit. The mag-

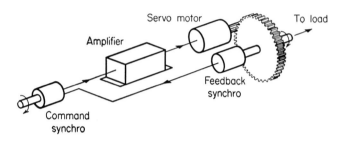

Fig. 10-4. Block diagram of a low-power positional servo system. (*Courtesy, Industrial Control Company.*)

netic amplifier draws power directly from the line, and meters it to the servo motor proportionally with the error signal.

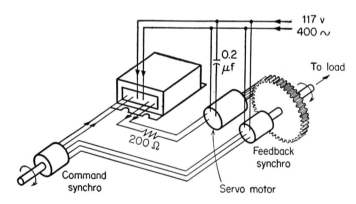

Fig. 10-5. System connections of a low-power positional servo system. (*Courtesy, Industrial Control Company.*)

The over-all schematic of a positioning servo system appears in Fig. 10-6. The load is a two-phase, 400-cycle per second servo motor. The magnetic amplifier consists of two identical reactors, SX_1 and SX_2. The 400-cycle control signal is applied to the grid of tube V_1, amplified, and applied to the grid of tube V_2. The output of V_2 is coupled simultaneously to the grids of V_3 and V_4. A 400-cycle reference voltage is applied between the cathodes of the same tubes, which are con-

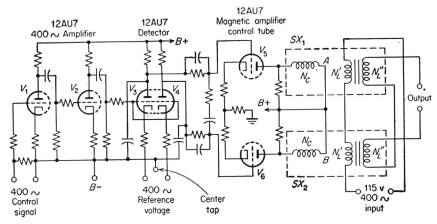

Fig. 10-6. Positioning servo system providing control power for instrument-type servo motor used in airborne military equipment. (*Courtesy, J. K. McKendry, General Precision Laboratory, Inc.*)

nected as a phase-sensitive detector. Any phase variation between the 400-cycle control signal and the reference voltage is sensed, and consequently causes d-c voltages of unequal magnitude to be applied to the grids of magnetic control amplifiers V_5 and V_6. If the control current of reactor A is increased and that of reactor B is decreased, the impedance of reactor A increases, while that of B decreases, and the output voltage of B will be correspondingly greater than that of A. A net voltage of B's polarity then appears across the output terminals. Conversely, a decrease in control current of reactor A and an increase in reactor B will yield an output of A polarity.

The resistance-capacitance network connected between the grids of amplifiers V_5 and V_6 acts to shape the frequency response of the amplifiers. This is necessary because of the energy storage effects contributed by the magnetic amplifier and by the interacting motor and magnetic amplifier.

10-4. Synchro signal adapter servo system

Figure 10-7, (a) and (b), illustrates a servo system in which angular input data are repeated with a minimum of position, velocity, or ac-

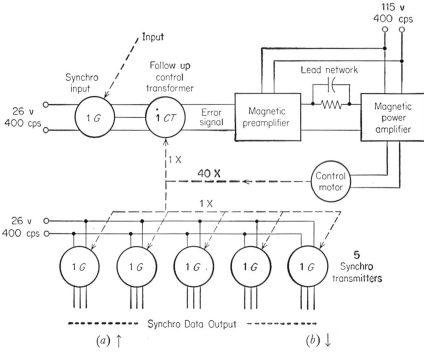

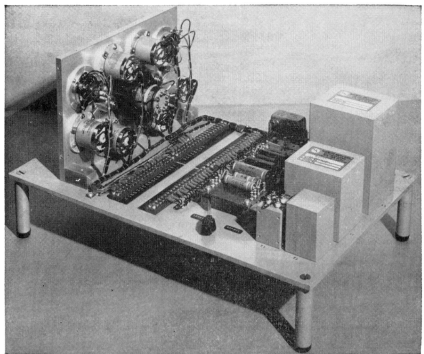

Fig. 10-7. (a) High-performance synchro signal adapter. (*After Magnetic Amplifiers, Inc.*) (b) Synchro signal adapter, cover removed. (*Courtesy, Magnetic Amplifiers, Inc.*)

celeration error. In this servo positioning system, input data are repeated by positioning a shaft which is coupled to the output synchro transmitters.

The angular position of the synchro input transmitter determines the voltage supplied to the follow-up control transformer. The control motor also feeds voltage to the control transformer. The difference in angular position between the synchro transmitter and the synchro control transformer is fed as an error voltage to the preamplifier. The preamplifier supplies a d-c output proportional to the magnitude of the error voltage with a polarity depending on the phase of the error signal. This output feeds the power amplifier, which drives the control motor in a direction to reduce the angular differences between the synchro transmitter and the synchro control transformer.

Five synchro transmitters are geared one-to-one to the follow-up control transformer. Their phase voltages track the angular position of the synchro control transformer and thus repeat the position of the synchro transmitter shaft. The lead network between the preamplifier output and the magnetic amplifier power input suppresses the tendency of the system to oscillate.

Although the preamplifier indicated in Fig. 10-7(a) is of the magnetic-amplifier type, other circuit applications may require the use of the vacuum-tube or transistor variety, as shown in Fig. 10-6. Vacuum tubes or transistors may be used for signal levels below the minimum required for proper magnetic-amplifier operation (below 10^{-10} watt). Another reason for vacuum-tube or transistor preamplifiers operating in conjunction with magnetic-amplifier output stages is that they perform satisfactorily in the presence of high-input impedances.

The performance specifications of this typical synchro signal-adapter servo system [Fig. 10-7(a)] may appear as follows:

Supply voltage..............	115 volts
Supply frequency...........	400 cycles per second
Input data.................	Shaft position
Static accuracy.............	0.2 degree
Maximum following speed...	450 degrees per second
Error at constant velocity inputs..................	At 20 degrees per second, 0.3 degree
	At 120 degrees per second, 0.5 degree
	At 300 degrees per second, 1.5 degree
Settling time after introducing 90-degree step............	6 cycles per second

10-5. Torque motor servo system

Magnetic servo amplifiers are frequently called upon to drive a torque motor (or torquer), which is an electromechanical device using a differential magnetic field to establish a mechanical force.

The operation of this device may be followed by reference to Fig. 10-8(a). A single-ended input voltage is applied to the magnetic

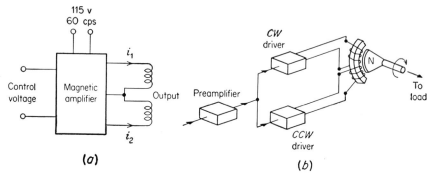

Fig. 10-8. (a) Magnetic amplifier operating into differential load as required for torquer. (b) Block diagram, torquer amplifier and actuator. (*Courtesy, Industrial Control Company.*)

amplifier, which has a dual-channel, three- or four-wire output. When the currents i_1 and i_2 are equal, the magnetic fluxes produced in the output windings are equal and opposite, and the total output flux is zero. At this time, the net torque produced by the torque motor is zero, and the load is not actuated. When i_1 is greater than i_2, the differential magnetic field produced interacts with the permanent magnet rotor of the torquer, and a torque is produced in the motor. When i_2 is greater than i_1, a torque is produced which drives the torquer in the reverse direction. The output torque is always proportional to the difference between the currents in the two coils. A block diagram of a torquer amplifier and actuator is shown in Fig. 10-8(b).

10-6. Magnetic servo amplifiers

Servo amplifiers are used to amplify the servo error signal to a power level capable of driving the servo actuator (error-correcting device) in the desired direction. The actuator can, of course, be any one of many different loads. One of the most common is the two-phase a-c servo motor. For proper operation, the servo motor requires that the phase of the voltage applied to the fixed field of the motor remain constant and 90 degrees out of phase with respect to the phase of the motor control field. The voltage applied to the fixed field comes directly from the line; that applied to the control field windings is supplied by the magnetic servo amplifier.

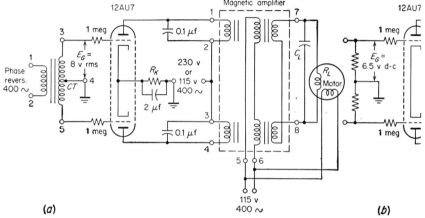

Fig. 10-9. (a) Magnetic servo amplifier operating in conjunction with vacuum-tube preamplifier. (*Courtesy, United Transformer Company.*) (b) Modifying the grid circuit for d-c control.

A magnetic servo amplifier operating in conjunction with a vacuum-tube preamplifier is shown in Fig. 10-9(a). In this circuit, a phase-reversible, 400-cycle control signal is applied to the primary of the input transformer. The secondary voltage is applied to the grids of the twin-triode connected in push-pull. The output of the preamplifier is supplied to the control windings of the magnetic amplifier, thus ultimately determining the motor operation. Capacitor C_L is chosen so as to effect a 90-degree phase angle between the voltages applied to the servo-motor windings.

Figure 10-9(a) illustrates the input circuit when an a-c control signal is to be used. Figure 10-9(b) shows the grid-circuit modification when d-c control is desired. A typical servo amplifier which may be used in this application is shown in Fig. 10-10(a) and (b).

10-7. High-speed magnetic servo amplifier

As a rule, conventional magnetic amplifiers are handicapped in their application to high-performance high-speed servo loops because

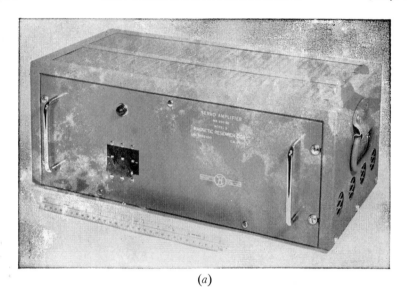

(a)

(b)

Fig. 10-10. Typical servo magnetic amplifier: (a) cover on; (b) cover removed. (*Courtesy, Magnetic Research Corporation.*)

of their lag in response. In many servo systems, the device must respond in one cycle of the a-c supply frequency or less.

Figure 10-11 illustrates a high-speed reset* magnetic servo amplifier, which has a fixed response time of one-half cycle of the line frequency, and is therefore suitable for direct amplification of a-c signals from synchros or other sources. To follow the operation of the

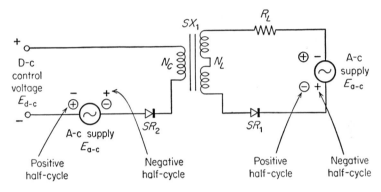

Fig. 10-11. High-performance half-wave reset magnetic servo amplifier.

reset circuit, assume that no signal control voltage is applied to the device. On the half-cycle when the a-c supply voltage has the circled polarities, rectifier SR_1 is conductive and current flows through the N_L winding of the reactor. The flux produced by this current (assuming that this is the positive half-cycle) approaches the positive upper knee of the B-H curve. Since rectifier SR_2 is nonconductive at this time, no flux is generated by the control winding N_C.

On the next, or negative half-cycle, rectifier SR_1 is nonconductive, but SR_2 conducts permitting current to the flow in the N_C windings. The flux produced now approaches the negative lower knee of the B-H curve. The negative half-cycle is called the reset half-cycle. As a result of this action, and in the absence of control voltage, the core flux fluctuates alternately between the upper and lower positions of the magnetization curve, while never reaching saturation at either end. Thus, the reactor impedance is high, and little current flows in either the load or control circuit.

Assume now that a control voltage, with the polarity indicated in Fig. 10-11, is applied to control circuit. This voltage opposes that of

---

* *Reset* refers to the fact that, in this circuit, the amount of the change is controlled during each alternate half-cycle, called the reset or negative half-cycle.

the signal voltage during the negative half-cycle, so that the flux produced during this time interval does not approach as near to the negative knee of the magnetization curve as it did in the absence of control voltage.

On the next, or positive half-cycle, rectifier SR_1 starts to conduct and the core flux starts to rise in the direction of the positive knee of the curve. Since the flux starting point is not at the negative knee of the curve, but rather at some point higher than this, as produced during the preceding negative half-cycle, the flux reaches core saturation during the positive half-cycle, and the impedance of the reactor decreases. As a result, an increased voltage appears across the load R_L. The amplitude of load voltage appearing on the positive half-cycle is, in effect, determined by the control voltage that had been applied to the control circuit on the preceding negative half-cycle, and the time of response of this magnetic amplifier is one half-cycle.

The characteristics of this circuit are such that it can be either a-c or d-c controlled, since only the control voltage appearing during the negative, or reset half-cycle is effective. Furthermore, the power gain of the circuit is high, since control current flows only when the core

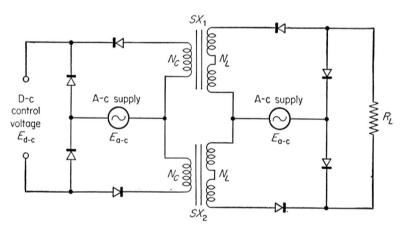

Fig. 10-12. Connection of two half-wave reset magnetic servo amplifiers for full-wave operation.

has reached magnetic saturation. The adaptation of the basic half-wave reset circuit to a full-wave network is shown in Fig. 10-12.

Reset magnetic amplifiers have been used to great advantage as a-c power amplifiers, synchro booster amplifiers, d-c power amplifiers, and computer elements.

REVIEW QUESTIONS

1. In the servomechanism block shown in Fig. 10-2, assume that the quantity to be regulated is a voltage which does not agree with the fixed reference voltage. Describe how the magnetic amplifiers in the servo system act to balance the loop.

2. What is the purpose of the phase-sensitive demodulator in Fig. 10-3(a)?

3. If the static plate current of V_5 in Fig. 10-6 is less than that of V_6, what happens to the circuit output?

4. The magnetic amplifier circuit shown in Fig. 10-11 is d-c controlled. Describe the circuit operation for an a-c controlled connection.

CHAPTER

11

Educational Magnetic Amplifiers

▀▄▀

11-1. Introduction

Because the magnetic amplifier has assumed a place of importance in control and other applications, the student of electronics must become familiar with its characteristics. To this end, educational magnetic amplifiers based on the breadboard principle have been developed, so that a teacher operating in conjunction with his student engineers (or the students themselves) can demonstrate the basic concepts of the magnetic device, and can illustrate its applications to many fundamental circuits. In addition, the unit can be used by development engineers for experimental purposes in industrial laboratories. Two such educational devices are described in this chapter.

11-2. Basic educational magnetic amplifier*

Figure 11-1(a) shows the basic schematic of the educational magnetic amplifier illustrated in Fig. 11-1(b). The multiple control, bias, and load windings of the reactors, as well as the rectifiers, are all ter-

---

* The educational magnetic amplifier discussed in this section is manufactured by Vickers Electric Division.

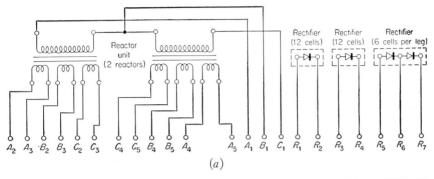

(a)

(b)

Fig. 11-1. (a) Schematic of breadboard-connected educational magnetic amplifier. (*Courtesy, Vickers Electric Division.*) (b) Educational magnetic amplifier (*Courtesy, Vickers Electric Division.*)

minated in screw-type terminals, so that the device may be connected in any of several circuits by simple means.

To illustrate how the unit may be used, Fig. 11-2(a) shows how the amplifier may be connected to operate into a d-c load under conditions of either a-c or d-c control. The load is shown in series with the reactors' center-tap. For a-c control, windings B_2-B_3 and B_3-B_5* are series-connected to an external a-c control source. For d-c control, windings C_2-C_3 and C_4-C_5, connected in series opposing, are joined to a d-c control voltage.

---

* The chassis terminals are marked with letters to assist the student engineer or technician in setting up new circuits.

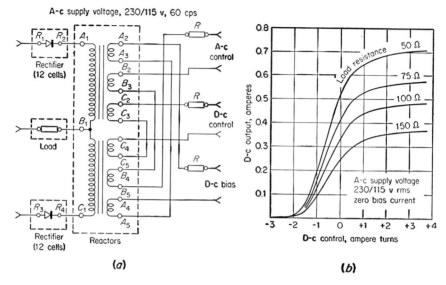

(a)   *(b)*

Fig. 11-2. (a) A-c or d-c controlled magnetic amplifier operating into d-c load. (*Courtesy, Vickers Electric Division.*) (b) Control characteristics showing effect of load variation. (*Courtesy, Vickers Electric Division.*)

Figures 11-3(a) and 11-4(a) are schematics of two other fundamental self-saturating circuits that may be connected using the components on the educational amplifier chassis. In the former circuit, the ampli-

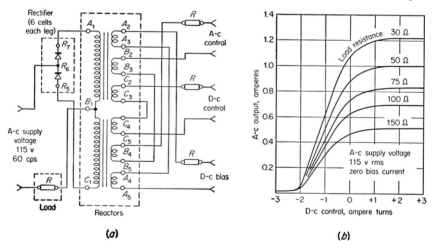

(a)   *(b)*

Fig. 11-3. (a) A-c or d-c controlled educational magnetic amplifier operating into a-c load. (*Courtesy, Vickers Electric Division.*) (b) Control characteristics showing effect of load variation. (*Courtesy, Vickers Electric Division.*)

fier is either a-c or d-c controlled and operates into an a-c load; the latter can also be controlled by a-c or d-c and, like the circuit of Fig. 11-2(a), operates into a d-c load.

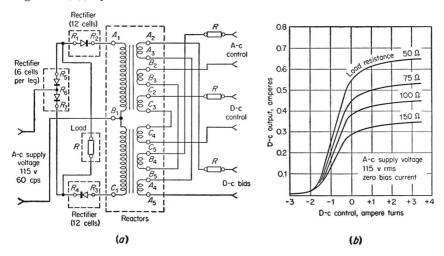

Fig. 11-4. (a) A-c or d-c controlled educational magnetic amplifier operating into d-c load. (*Courtesy, Vickers Electric Division.*) (b) Control characteristics showing effect of load variation. (*Courtesy, Vickers Electric Division.*)

The student may use any of the illustrated circuits to plot the static characteristics of the magnetic amplifier. As an example, to do this for conditions of d-c control for Fig. 11-2(a), an ammeter is connected in series with the load and another in series with the appropriate control winding. Then, by using an adjustable resistance in series with the control voltage source, the control current is varied and the change in control current observed. These figures are plotted on a graph with the d-c output in amperes as the ordinate and the control d-c ampere turns as the abscissa. The value of this latter is obtained by multiplying the control current in amperes by the number of turns in the applicable control windings. (The C winding has 35 turns while the A and B windings have 100 each.) Negative values of ampere turns are obtained by reversing the connections to the C_2 and C_5 terminals. This procedure is repeated for different values of load resistance, so that a family of curves is obtained, similar to that of Fig. 11-2(b). When the static characteristics are plotted for Figs. 11-3(a) and 11-4(a), the families of curves shown in Figs. 11-3(b) and 11-4(b) are obtained.

Using any of the illustrated circuits, the student engineer can gain familiarity with the operating characteristics of the elementary magnetic amplifier device. In addition to plotting curves representing the static characteristics, experiments to determine the following amplifier characteristics can also be conducted:

1. Load characteristics: to determine the internal impedance and the optimum load for a magnetic amplifier. (The power output of the amplifier is dependent upon the value of the load into which it operates. When the load impedance equals the source impedance, the power output is at its maximum.)

2. Control characteristics: to determine the effect of a-c and d-c control on magnetic-amplifier performance. (A-c control can be used if the control windings are so connected that the harmonic component in the control winding is eliminated. It will also be noted that more a-c than d-c is required for control.)

3. Self-saturation characteristics: to determine the characteristics derived from the use of internal feedback. (The control power requirement is reduced.)

These are just a few of the experiments which can be conducted with the device of Fig. 11-2. In addition to the other characteristics which may be explored, applications of the amplifier also can be examined. For example, a number of experiments can be set up to explore the application of the magnetic amplifier to the voltage and current

Fig. 11-5(a). Magnetic amplifier servo demonstrator. (*Courtesy, Magnetic Amplifiers, Inc.*)

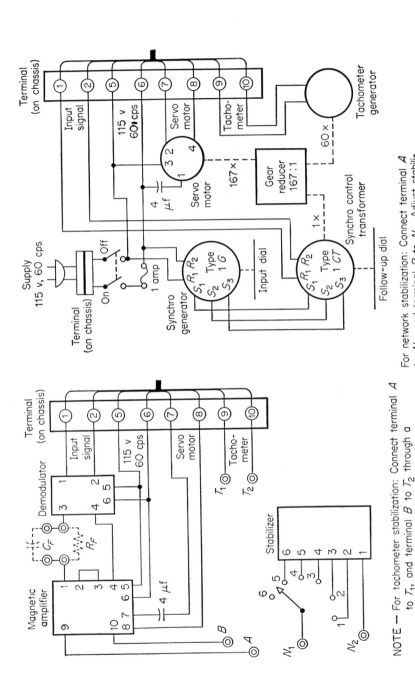

Fig. 11-5(b). Schematic diagram of magnetic amplifier servo demonstrator comprising amplifier unit (left) and gear train unit (right). (*Courtesy, Magnetic Amplifiers, Inc.*)

regulation of small generators, motor speed control, positioning con-control, and so forth.

11-3. Magnetic amplifier servo demonstrator*

A magnetic amplifier servo demonstrator [Fig. 11-5(a)] has been designed for educational use and research in the application of the magnetic amplifier to the servomechanism field. A schematic of the demonstrator, which is built on two chassis, is shown in Fig. 11-5(b).

The device consists of a gear train unit and an amplifier unit which operate in conjunction with each other to produce a complete magnetic amplifier positioning unit. The amplifier unit comprises a demodulator (to convert a-c input signals into direct current), a high-gain magnetic amplifier, and a stabilization network. The gear train unit consists of a servo motor, a synchro generator, a synchro control transformer, a d-c tachometer generator, a gear train providing a 167:1 reduction between motor and output dials, and dials indicating the angular position of the input and output shafts.

Circuit stabilization may be accomplished in this device by means of a passive network or by a d-c tachometer signal. Terminals are provided so that resistance and capacitance can be added to modify the system performance characteristic.

The magnetic amplifier servo demonstrator can be used to perform experiments of the following type: open-loop (steady-state, d-c signal); sinusoidal response; transient response; repetitive transients; and others.

---

* The magnetic amplifier servo demonstrator discussed in this section is manufactured by Magnetic Amplifiers, Incorporated.

CHAPTER

12

Miscellaneous Circuits
and Applications

12-1. Introduction

Many and varied applications of the magnetic amplifier device have been illustrated and described in the preceding chapters. However, as indicated previously, the total number of both actual and potential applications is almost limitless, so that no single text could possibly encompass them all.

This chapter covers certain other magnetic amplifier applications, some of which bear close relation to those discussed in earlier chapters, and others which are quite unique. A-c and d-c voltage regulators, dimmers, high-frequency reactor circuits, and others are described on the following pages.

12-2. A-c voltage regulation

In many cases, amplidynes* are operated in conjunction with

---

* The amplidyne is an externally driven d-c generator. The short circuit placed across two of its four brushes produces a device of high amplification and rapid response. The amplidyne generally has multiple control fields wound on the same pole structure, so that it can respond to several control signals simultaneously or separately. It must be remembered that the amplidyne is only one of the machines which are classified as rotating or rotary amplifiers.

magnetic amplifiers to provide close control over voltage, current, speed, or position. When used for voltage control, this circuit combination permits the output voltage of a power system to be held constant; for current control, it provides a means by which a constant tension or torque can be maintained, as in rolling, winding, and drawing operations; for speed control, it enables separate machines to be synchronized, or maintained at a preset speed; for position control, it holds the position of moving materials automatically.

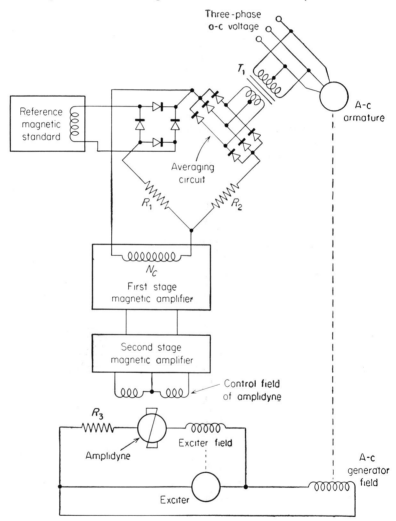

Fig. 12-1(a). Simplified diagram of a voltage regulator using a magnetically controlled amplidyne. (*Courtesy, General Electric Company.*)

Figure 12-1(a) is a simplified diagram showing how two stages of cascaded magnetic amplification are used to control an amplidyne, the output of which, in turn, is used to regulate the a-c voltage of a hydraulic generator [Fig. 12-1(b)] rated 75,000 kva at 1800 rpm. The regulator circuit holds the terminal voltage of the generator constant despite variations in load.

Fig. 12-1(b). Million-pound rotor in assembly of hydraulic generator which is regulated by a magnetically controlled amplidyne. (*Courtesy*, *General Electric Company.*)

The three-phase output of the a-c generator is applied through transformer T_1 and an averaging circuit consisting of six rectifiers. This circuit is one arm in a bridge, the other three arms being resistor R_1, resistor R_2, and the network comprising the reference magnetic standard and four rectifiers. Basically the reference is a single-phase, series-connected saturable reactor which is brought to saturation by a built-in permanent magnet. Its output is, for all intents and purposes, independent of line and load fluctuations.

When the a-c generator output agrees with the reference, the bridge is balanced and no current flows through the N_c control winding of the first magnetic amplifier. When, however, the generator output deviates from the standard, the bridge is unbalanced, and voltage appears across the control winding of the first stage of magnetic amplification. The output of this stage is applied to and amplified by the second stage.

The load into which the second magnetic amplifier operates is the control field of the amplidyne, which in turn sets the level of amplidyne output. This output aids or opposes the exciter field voltage, thereby changing the generator field excitation in such a direction as to return the generator armature voltage to normal.

12-3. Power supply voltage regulation

Commercial power supplies which produce a regulated d-c output, held constant despite wide changes in line voltage or load current, utilize magnetic amplifiers because of their reliability and sensitivity. The simplified version of such a d-c regulator is shown in Fig. 12-2(a).

The a-c supply voltage which may, of course, fluctuate depending upon line conditions, is applied to transformer T_1. The primary of this transformer and capacitor C_1 form a resonant circuit. During each half-cycle of the applied voltage, the core of T_1 is driven to saturation, so that the total flux change in the core is constant with respect to time. Any line voltage variation which occurs after the core has reached saturation can cause no further flux change, and thus cannot affect the voltage induced in the secondary of T_1.

Capacitor C_1 is charged during each half-cycle of the line voltage. If, after the charge time, a negative line transient occurs, the capacitor discharges through the primary of T_1, thereby increasing the voltage induced into the secondary, and compensating for the decreased line voltage. If a positive line transient appears, inductor L will absorb

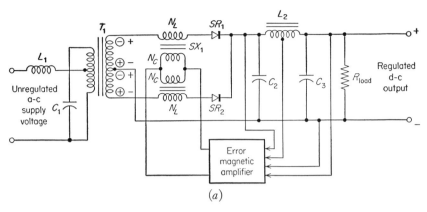

(a)

(b)

Fig. 12-2. (a) Automatic voltage regulation of a d-c power supply using two magnetic amplifiers. (*Courtesy, Magnetic Research Corporation.*) (b) Self-contained regulated d-c power supply. (*Courtesy, Magnetic Research Corporation.*)

the increased voltage beyond that necessary to saturate the transformer core. However, if the line or load variations are sufficiently severe, d-c voltage variations might appear in the output despite the action of T_1, and thus the need for additional regulation.

To follow the action of the circuit in the subsequent regulation, assume that the device is operating during the half-cycle having the circled polarity shown at the secondary of T_1. At this time, electrons flow through the filter network made up of components C_2, C_3, and L_2, rectifier SR_2, and one load winding of saturable reactor SX_1 to the positive potential point of the transformer. On the next half-cycle, electrons flow through the same filter network, rectifier SR_1, and the other load winding of the reactor. Over the full cycle, the rectifiers acting in conjunction with the filter network produce the d-c output which is applied to the load.

The control windings of reactor SX_1 which, of course, determine the impedance of SX_1 and the consequent output voltage are controlled by the output of a second magnetic amplifier (in the block called error magnetic amplifier). This amplifier has three control windings, so connected as to sense the output voltage, the load current, and the rate of change of the output voltage. In this manner, all load variations affect the output of the error magnetic amplifier which, by connection to the control windings of SX_1, acts to produce voltage compensation. As a result, d-c regulation having a short recovery time with respect to transients is obtained.

Figure 12-2(b) is a picture of a typical regulated power supply similar to that described above.

12-4. D-c magnetic amplifiers

In many industrial telemetering and instrumentation applications, a stable amplifier is required for amplifying the low-level signals obtained from strain gauges, thermocouples, resistance thermometer bridges, or photocells. The magnetic amplifier, because of its reliability and stability, has been applied to this function.

Figure 12-3(a) shows the fundamental connection diagram of a magnetic amplifier used for low-level d-c amplification. The device is excited by a 400-cycle per second a-c supply voltage (pins 5 and 6). The d-c control signal input is applied to pins 1 and 2, and the amplified output is taken from pins 3 and 4. A bias winding (pins 7 and 8) is provided to elevate the zero signal level in order to accommodate duo-directional signals. (No bias is required if the signals are unidirectional.) If it is so desired, the bias winding may be used in order to introduce feedback into the device.

Figure 12-3(b) illustrates the connection diagram of a d-c magnetic amplifier which may be used in the absence of an available a-c supply. In this device, d-c supply voltage is applied to pins 5 and 6. A transistorized oscillator, housed within the unit, operates on this d-c supply, and produces the a-c excitation required for the magnetic

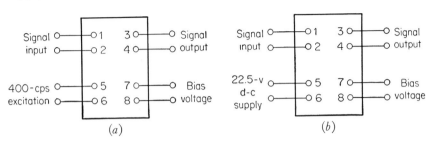

(a)   (b)

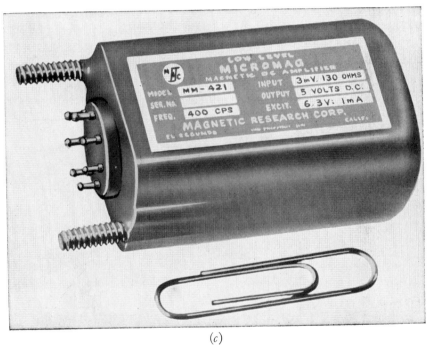

(c)

Fig. 12-3. Connection diagram and picture of low-level d-c signal amplifiers used for telemetering and instrumentation applications. (*Courtesy, Magnetic Research Corporation.*) (a) Connections for operating from a-c supply. (b) Connections for operating from d-c supply. (c) A-c operated d-c supply.

amplifier operation. All other connections are identical to those of the amplifier as described for (a).

Figure 12-3(c) shows a typical low-level d-c magnetic-amplifier device.

12-5. Magnetic amplifier dimmer

In Chapter 5, the use of the saturable reactor as applied to the control of theatre lighting was described. However, the magnetic amplifier has been applied to the same function, and with great success. The number of ampere turns required to control the magnetic amplifier is considerably less than that needed for a saturable reactor, thus increasing the speed of response of the device, and decreasing its comparative size.

The elementary diagram of a magnetic amplifier dimmer is shown in Fig. 12-4(a) and a picture of the unit appears in Fig. 12-4(b). Note that the device consists of a magnetic preamplifier which controls a magnetic power amplifier, which in turn determines the voltage developed across the lamp load. When the a-c supply voltage is such that point R is negative, electrons flow through the output (load)

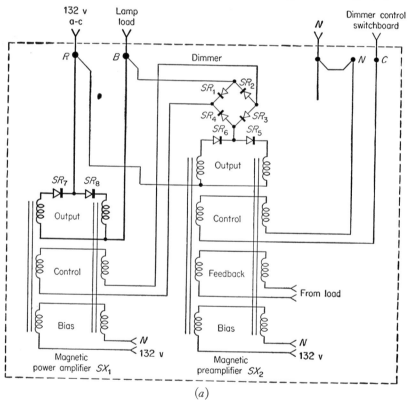

(a)

Fig. 12-4(a). Simplified diagram of two-stage magnetic amplifier dimmer circuit. (*Courtesy, Vickers Electric Division.*)

(b)

(c)

Fig. 12-4 (cont.). (b) Two-stage magnetic amplifier dimmer. (*Courtesy,*
Vickers Electric Division.) (c) Simplified diagram of one section of a four-
section dimmer control switchboard. (*Courtesy, Vickers Electric Division.*)

windings of reactor SX_2, rectifier SR_5, rectifier SR_3, the control windings of reactor SX_1, rectifier SR_1, and back through the lamp load.
Current also flows from point R through rectifier SR_7 and the output
windings of reactor SX_1 through the lamp load. The voltage developed across the load is determined by the voltage applied from the
dimmer control switchboard to the control winding of reactor SX_2.
The flux produced by this control winding determines the impedance

of the output windings of SX_2, which controls the voltage developed across the control windings of SX_2. In turn, these set the level of the impedance of the output windings of SX_2, thereby fixing the load lamp voltage.

To obtain full voltage across the lamps when maximum brightness is required, the a-c supply voltage is increased to 132 volts by means of an autotransformer. In this manner, and assuming that 120 volts are needed for full brightness, the 12-volt boost compensates for the drop across the reactors.

Figure 12-4(c) is the simplified diagram of one section of a four-section dimmer control switchboard which may be used in conjunction with the dimmer circuit described for (a). The settings of S_1 and S_2 determine which of the control potentiometers are in the circuit, thereby determining the amplitude of the voltage at terminal C_1 which is applied to the dimmer circuit.

12-6. High-frequency saturable reactors

Special saturable reactors have been developed which operate on high-frequency a-c supply voltages, and which may prove to be of value in high-speed digital data-processing systems. In general, these special reactors, called magnistors,* may be divided into two types, transient and permanent.

Basically, the transient magnistor operates in similar fashion to the conventional low-frequency saturable reactor. Two coils, one for control and one for load, are wound on a ferromagnetic core, and are designed for use with an a-c supply of approximately 15 megacycles [Fig. 12-5(a)].

The control winding is placed on the core in such a manner that the control current produces a flux which affects the core magnetization, and thereby sets the level of inductance of the signal windings. Under normal operating conditions, the impedance is largely inductive. By means of the control coil, the inductance of the signal windings, and hence the impedance of the reactor, can be made to vary in a ratio of 500 to 1 in certain switch applications.

The transient-type magnistor may be designed with multiple signal and control windings. It can also be equipped with inhibit coils which destroy the influence of the control coil if the latter is

---

* Trademark of Potter Instrument Co., Inc.

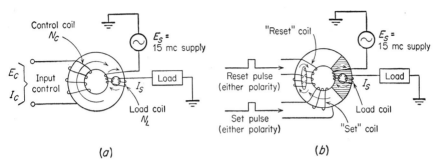

Fig. 12-5. High-frequency saturable reactors: (a) transient type; (b) permanent type. (*Courtesy, Potter Instrument Company.*)

energized, but have no effect otherwise. Thus, the magnistor can be useful in large arrays to perform complex logical and mathematical functions.

The permanent type of magnistor consists of three windings on a ferromagnetic core. One is a load winding similar to that used in the transient magnistor, while the others are control windings normally designated "set" and "reset." The load winding has two possible impedances. A low impedance exists if a specified minimum current has passed through the coil in either direction. A higher impedance exists if a specified minimum current has passed through the reset coil. Either condition persists until the other is re-established.

The magnistor is essentially a high-frequency saturable reactor. Experimental high-frequency magnetic amplifiers have also been developed, capable of operation in the region of 100 megacycles. Because the gain of these devices is approximately equal to that experienced at lower frequencies, while their time constant is decreased, the figure of merit of the amplifiers is high.

One of the problems encountered in the development of high-frequency amplifiers is the unavailability of high-frequency power sources (although future developments in transistor circuitry may solve the problem). A second obstacle is the large capacitance of the dry-disc rectifiers used in internal-feedback amplifiers. In the case of selenium rectifiers, for example, the shunt capacitance of the plates acts as a short circuit at high frequencies, so that the rectifier efficiency is reduced radically. If the point-contact type of germanium rectifier diodes is used, the shunt capacity is decreased, but the power-handling capabilities of the circuits are also decreased.

12-7. Regulating a d-c generator

Figure 12-6 indicates a circuit in which variations in direct generator excitation current, caused by changes in speed or load, are compensated for by means of a magnetic amplifier device. The mag-

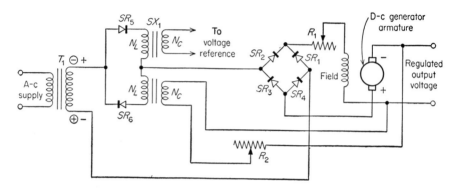

Fig. 12-6. Use of a magnetic amplifier to regulate the output of a d-c generator.

netic amplifier has two control windings, one of which is controlled by the voltage from the generator output, and the other of which is fed from a reference voltage. When the two control voltages agree, the generator is operating at its rated value. When these voltages differ, regulation action occurs to bring the output back to the rated value.

When the voltage across the secondary of transformer T_1 has the circled polarity, electrons flow through rectifier SR_6, a load winding of reactor SX_1, rectifier SR_3, the armature of the d-c generator, its field winding, rheostat R_1, and rectifier SR_1 to the transformer. On the next half-cycle, current flows in the same direction through the armature and the field, and through the other load winding of the reactor.

The two control windings are wound oppositely to each other. Thus, when the armature voltage is equal to the reference voltage, the fluxes produced by these windings cancel, and the reactor impedance is high. As a result, only a small portion of the voltage derived from the a-c supply appears across the generator and field.

When circuit conditions are such that the armature voltage is less than that of the reference source, control flux appears in the reactor core and the reactor impedance diminishes. As a result, increased current flows through the generator field, boosting its excitation, and thus restoring the generator voltage to its normal value. When the generator voltage starts to increase above the rated value, the magnetic amplifier booster action ceases and the generator returns to its normal output.

12-8. Temperature control

Figure 12-7 illustrates the schematic of a magnetic amplifier which can be used for general-purpose temperature control, or as an alarm and detection device. Its control voltage may be a signal derived from a temperature-sensitive resistor or resistors connected in a bridge circuit. The output of the magnetic amplifier operates a relay circuit,

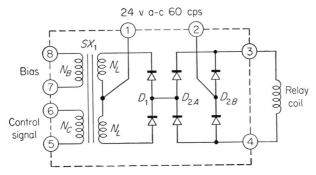

Fig. 12-7. Magnetic amplifier energizing a relay. (*Courtesy, Warren Manufacturing Company, Inc.*)

which can be used to trigger any desired control function. The temperature at which the magnetic amplifier causes the relay to energize can be determined by adjusting the fixed arms of the bridge, or by applying voltage to the bias winding of the magnetic amplifier.

As shown in the diagram, the magnetic amplifier of Fig. 12-7 is self-contained, and has 8 external connections: 2 for control voltage; 2 for a-c supply voltage (24 volts a-c is indicated); 2 for bias; and 2 for output. In the absence of control voltage, the impedance of the reactor SX_1 is high, and only a small portion of the supply voltage appears across the external relay coil. As control voltage is applied, the SX_1 impedance decreases, and the voltage across the relay coil increases, until it energizes.

12-9. Audio amplification

A four-reactor circuit is shown in Fig. 12-8 in which magnetic amplifiers are applied to the amplification of audio voltages. The audio

output of the microphone is fed to the series-connected control windings of reactors SX_1 through SX_4. The load windings, through their
respective rectifiers SR_1 through SR_4 (connected so as to produce

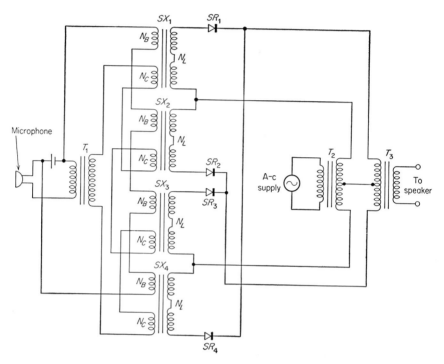

Fig. 12-8. Magnetic amplifier for audio amplification.

internal feedback), are joined to the secondary of power transformer T_2.

The impedance of the reactors fluctuates as determined by the a-c
audio voltage applied to the control windings of the reactors. In this
manner, amplified audio variations are coupled to the primary of
audio output transformers T_3, and hence through the transformer to
the speaker voice coil.

A primary disadvantage of the magnetic audio amplifier lies in the
fact that the a-c supply frequency must be considerably higher than
the highest audio frequency it is desired to reproduce. As a result, the
a-c supply must be in the form of an oscillator, designed to operate at
15 kilocycles or higher.

12-10. Magnetic reference standard

A special type of saturable reactor may be used as part of a magnetic device to provide a voltage or current reference for a regulating system. In this circuit, shown in Fig. 12-9, a three-legged reactor

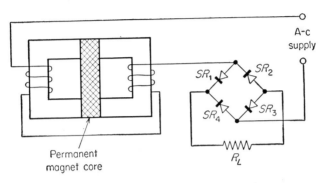

Fig. 12-9. Magnetic reference standard.

having a center core of permanent-magnetic material is used. The two outer cores are of conventional magnetic material.

The permanent-magnet portion of the special reactor sets up a fixed magnetic field, such as would be provided by the application of a constant d-c voltage to reactor control windings. As a result, the impedance of the device is held constant, and the output, taken across the load R_L, is essentially constant.

REVIEW QUESTION

1. The output of the averaging circuit in Fig. 12-1(a) is compared to the output of the magnetic reference standard. Assume polarities and discuss how this portion of the regulator circuit operates.

Properties and Characteristics
of Magnetic Amplifiers

13-1. Introduction

Within a relatively short period of time, the general usage of the magnetic amplifier has become truly widespread. This is more remarkable when one considers the large number of present applications in which the device is utilized, despite the fact that the potentialities of the magnetic amplifier have scarcely been explored.

The sudden eminence of this type of amplifier stems in part from the technological improvements that have occurred in recent years in magnetic materials and metallic rectifiers. Thus research in the magnetic field led to the need for, and the consequent production of, magnetic core materials with narrow, rectangular hysteresis curves. These materials improved the design characteristics of the magnetic amplifier device so that its use in the control, regulation, and instrumentation fields became practicable. Furthermore, research on selenium, germanium, and silicon rectifiers led to the development of improved rectifiers which, when taken in conjunction with the newer core materials, greatly extended the scope of application of the magnetic amplifier.

13-2. Advantages of magnetic amplifiers

Although the magnetic amplifier will never replace the electron tube, it has certain specific advantages which, in many cases, make its use almost mandatory. Some of the principal characteristics of the magnetic amplifier which may be considered as advantages in specific applications follow.

Ruggedness. The magnetic amplifier is an extremely rugged device and, as such, is virtually vibration- and shock-proof. Because of its sturdy quality, it lends itself to applications in which reliability must be maintained in the presence of shock and impact, and in which the requirements for continuity of service are severe. Furthermore, its use reduces spare parts requirements and decreases the problem of maintenance, e.g., comparable to that of an iron-core transformer. In addition, the magnetic amplifier has no moving parts, which increases its reliability (no moving parts or contacts to wear) and permits it to be used in potted-type construction or hermetically sealed. In effect, the life expectancy of the magnetic amplifier is limited by that of the associated rectifiers. These rectifiers may be rated at 60,000 hours or more under normal conditions.

Instant Availability. The magnetic amplifier contains no filaments. Because of this, it requires no warm-up time, so that the amplifier is immediately available for operation and control when the device is turned on. This is extremely advantageous for any applications in which instantaneous control is a prime requisite. Also, the standby power requirements of the over-all equipment are reduced.

In addition, the fact that the magnetic amplifier operates without filaments means that there is one less item to become inoperative, i.e., no filaments to burn out, and hence its reliability is enhanced further. Thus it can be expected to give long and dependable service.

High Efficiency. The magnetic amplifier has an over-all efficiency in the order of 75 per cent. This figure may be compared with the plate efficiency of an electron tube, which is generally 50 per cent or less; it can be seen that the magnetic amplifier's efficiency is relatively high. Furthermore, the filament power requirement of a tube lowers the tube's over-all efficiency even more. For low-power electron-tube amplifiers, the filament power is often 20 times greater than the output power of the stage.

As a corollary of high efficiency, the heat generated internally in a magnetic amplifier is extremely small, and may be considered negligible for most applications. As a result, the magnetic amplifier requires little ventilation and can even operate with a high degree of safety in compartments.

Isolation. Because of its operating characteristics, the input and output circuits of the magnetic amplifier are completely isolated from each other. This is true whether single or multiple inputs are used. This isolation is of great advantage in many applications, as for example in the instrumentation and measurement field. In addition, the isolation permits several input signals, acting for control, to be mixed at different levels.

High Gain. The use of regenerative feedback in the magnetic amplifier makes it possible to obtain extremely high gains in a single unit. Power gains in the order of magnitude of 10^6 or 10^7 can be reached in one device. Larger gains can be obtained by cascading. Thus the devices are highly sensitive and many are suitable for operation from signal sources with an input power as low as 10^{-8} watt. (In those cases where the input power is below this level, electron-tube or transistor preamplifiers may be used prior to the magnetic amplifiers.)

Input and Output Impedances. The magnetic amplifier can be designed to operate with a wide range of control circuit impedances. For example, magnetic amplifiers operating with a 60-cycle a-c supply may have an input impedance as low as 1 ohm* (or less) and as high as 100,000 ohms. Typical values of input impedances for common commercial magnetic amplifiers range from about 250 ohms to approximately 6500 ohms. The output impedance of the same device also extends over a relatively wide range, from about 5 to 5000 ohms. The minimum output impedance occurs when the core is fully saturated; the impedance value at this time is approximately the d-c resistance of the core windings and the rectifiers.

For magnetic amplifiers operating on a 400-cycle supply voltage, the range of input and output impedances necessarily is not as wide. As an example, typical input values of common magnetic amplifiers may range between 750 and 5000 ohms. This should be expected

---

* The magnetic amplifier is extremely suitable for low-impedance inputs, in marked contrast to the electron-tube amplifier. It is thus capable of being used to great advantage with inputs from thermocouples, photocells, strain gages, inductive pick-ups, etc.

since the addition of a large number of windings at this higher supply frequency will lead to the production of undesirable stray and distributed capacity effects.

Stability. The inherent noise level of the magnetic amplifier is quite low (owing in large part to the relatively low input impedance), and as a matter of fact is substantially less than the minimum signal power encountered in most practical applications. This minimum power level is determined in practice by considerations of stability and drift, and for magnetic amplifiers may be in the order of magnitude of 10^{-9} watt. Because the inputs are considerably larger than the noise level, the magnetic amplifier is usually free of drift problems, and its long-term stability is excellent. The stability and freedom from drift may be improved even more by using symmetrical push-pull magnetic amplifiers. The stability of the magnetic amplifier is further enhanced in that it is not affected greatly by fluctuations in the power supply voltage, as is an electron-tube amplifier.

Adaptability. The magnetic amplifier device has many miscellaneous characteristics, each of which may be considered as an advantage in itself. Each of the advantages listed below adds to the adaptability of the unit.

1. The magnetic amplifier core can be built in any shape, permitting the unit to be installed in a confined area. The number of core configurations is almost limitless.
2. The gain of the magnetic amplifier is varied simply by changing the amplitude of the control voltage. The leads connected to the control windings are relatively insensitive to stray and fluctuating fields.
3. Separate windings, which are electrically isolated from all other windings, may be wound on the magnetic amplifier to permit the introduction of feedback (positive to obtain increased gain and negative to obtain increased frequency response) or to permit the application of several control signals.
4. The magnetic amplifier can be used in conjunction with the electron tube, thereby increasing the versatility of both. A combination of circuits often provides an excellent solution for certain problems.

13-3. Disadvantages of magnetic amplifiers

Although the magnetic amplifier has the large number of advantages listed here, it also has certain disadvantages. It is hoped that these will be eliminated, or at least reduced, as the result of future experimentation and design. Some of the primary limitations follow.

Time of Response. The magnetic amplifier does not provide an instantaneous response; there is a finite time interval between the instant at which the control voltage is applied to the input circuit and the moment when the output voltage reaches its new value as determined by the input control voltage. In general, the time constant of the magnetic amplifier is quite long when compared to that of the electron-tube circuit. This lag is disadvantageous in those applications where a short response is a necessity, as in certain types of automatic control or high-performance servomechanisms, but does not enter into the picture in those cases where the time response of other portions of a control system are greater than that of the magnetic amplifier.

The response of the typical magnetic amplifier is approximately 2 to 30 cycles, although certain special circuits have a response less than 2 cycles. Thus, if the a-c supply frequency is 60 cycles and the magnetic amplifier under consideration has a response of 2 cycles, it will take about 33 milliseconds before the output voltage responds fully to changes in the input control signal.

If, on the other hand, the a-c supply frequency is 400 cycles and the magnetic amplifier has a response of 2 cycles, the response lag will be approximately 5 milliseconds. Thus the magnetic amplifier lag will decrease as the supply frequency increases. A second advantage of using a high supply frequency, in addition to the decreased response, is that it permits the physical size of the magnetic amplifier to be reduced.

Frequency Response. A present disadvantage of the magnetic amplifier is that its upper frequency response is severely limited, since the control signal can be only a fraction of the a-c supply frequency. This obviously hampers the application of the device as an audio-frequency amplifier. However, this disadvantage may be overcome by the development of magnetic amplifiers which are capable of operating in the presence of high-frequency supplies. Actually some experimentation has been performed in an attempt to extend the frequency response, and in one circuit using a specially designed magnetic amplifier a supply excitation frequency of 3 megacycles was applied. This device responded to a pulse repetition frequency of 400 kilocycles. In passing, it should be noted that this appears to represent the upper frequency limit of the magnetic amplifier at present, owing largely to the high eddy-current core losses and losses caused by distributed capacity effects encountered at these frequencies.

Size. In its present state of development, and specifically for units operating on a 60-cycle a-c supply, the magnetic amplifier is generally larger and somewhat more bulky than the device it replaces. This is true at the 60-cycle frequency since the core size and weight, and hence the dimension of the magnetic amplifier, are inversely proportional to the supply frequency. However, the size of a magnetic amplifier designed for operation on higher supply frequencies is small, and, depending upon the specific supply frequency, may be smaller than the device it replaces.

Cost. At present, the price of the individual magnetic amplifier is relatively high in relation to the unit it replaces in the circuit. This is understandable, since only the surface of the magnetic amplifier field has been scratched, and the device is not yet in full production. As more design data become available on the magnetic amplifiers, and as the number and scope of applications of the unit increase, production will rise undoubtedly, with a subsequent decrease in per-unit cost. In addition, it must be remembered that the cost for research of any new component is added to the price of the device; thus, when the research time on the magnetic amplifier decreases, the amplifier price will also decrease.

13-4. Rating specifications

Magnetic amplifiers are rated and described by means of various specifications which can be subdivided into two major categories: mechanical and electrical. Many of the individual terms are listed below, and are explained when they are not completely obvious. Some of the mechanical specifications which are used to describe a magnetic amplifier follow:

1. Physical dimensions: the over-all dimensions of the magnetic amplifier in height, width, and depth, usually given in inches such as $1\frac{5}{8}'' \times 1\frac{7}{8}'' \times 2\frac{1}{8}''$.
2. Mounting dimensions: the dimensions locating the mounting holes, bolts, or screws for fastening the device to a chassis, usually given in inches such as $\frac{3}{4}'' \times 1\frac{1}{4}''$.
3. Weight: usually given in pounds.

4. Temperature range: the ambient temperature range over which the magnetic amplifier can operate efficiently and with stability. Usually given in degrees centigrade, such as $-60°C$ to $+100°C$. The rated temperature rise of magnetic amplifier components is in accordance with established rise ratings for other electrical components.

5. Cutout: specification for the diameter of the hole that must be cut in the chassis so that electrical connection can be made to the magnetic amplifier terminals. Used only when the magnet amplifier connections are made through the base (chassis side) of the magnetic amplifier.

Some of the electrical specifications which describe a magnetic amplifier follow:

1. Supply voltage: the a-c source voltage which appears, in part, across the load windings. Although the supply is usually 115 volts, the magnetic amplifier can be designed for operation on other voltages. The rated supply voltage defines that voltage at which the device can operate continuously for any value of control and load currents within its rating without exceeding the established rating of any associated components.

2. Supply frequency: the frequency of the supply voltage applied to the load windings. Typical values are 60 and 400 cycles per second, but high-frequency units have been designed. For low supply frequencies the size of the amplifier varies inversely with the frequency. Thus a 50-watt amplifier operating on 60 cycles is approximately 6 times larger than a 50-watt amplifier operating on 400 cycles.

3. Output: the output appearing across the load into which the magnetic amplifier is operating. The output is given in terms of voltage and wattage, maximum values. The maximum output voltage is practically the same as the supply voltage. The maximum power output is determined primarily by the design of the magnetic amplifier.

4. Signal input: the input to the control windings required to produce full power (voltage) output. The signal input may be given in terms of current, voltage, or power.

5. Power gain: the ratio between the power output and the power input.

6. Quiescent signal output (zero signal output): the output appearing across the load in the absence of signal input. This current value may exceed a rated value in certain applications, thus requiring the use of compensating windings or push-pull operation.

7. Input impedance: the impedance of the control windings.

8. Output impedance: the impedance of the load windings.
9. Time of response: the time in cycles or seconds required to reach 63 per cent of the final value when a step change in voltage is applied to the input. For power gains of 1000 to 5000, the response time typically may be from 2 to 4 cycles.
10. Figure of merit: the ratio between the power gain and its time of response. The addition of positive feedback reduces the control power required for a given output, and thereby increases the figure of merit.

13-5. Commercial data

In order to give the reader some understanding of the manner in which data on magnetic amplifiers are presented, some of these data have been collected, and appear in Tables 13-1 through 13-5. This information has been extracted from the brochures of two manufacturers of commercial magnetic amplifiers, Tables 13-1 and 13-2 from one, and Tables 13-3 through 13-5 from the other.* It must be emphasized that the inclusion of the following data is not to be construed as a recommendation of these particular products by the author or as complete information on the products produced by the manufacturers.

---

* The information in Tables 13-1 and 13-2 is abridged from material supplied by Magnetic Amplifiers, Incorporated, and in Tables 13-3 through 13-5 from information forwarded by the Freed Transformer Company, Incorporated.

Table 13-1. 60-cps Magnetic Amplifiers[*]

Supply voltage: 115 volts[a]
Output voltage: 115 volts, a-c phase reversible[b]

Model number	Notes	Output (watts)	Maximum power gain[c]	Signal required for full power output	Input impedance (ohms)[c]	Typical motor load[d] Manufacturer and type number
MA-1001	b			0.1 v, a-c	$j1500$	Transicoil Corp. 6600
MA-60201-	b	2	2.2×10^5	b	b	Kollsman Inst. Corp. 1515-0101
MA-60501-	b	5	2.4×10^5	b	b	Kollsman Inst. Corp.
MA-60505-CY	b, e	5	5×10^4	1.2 ma, d-c	900	951-0160
MA-61001-	b	10	5.2×10^4	b	b	Kollsman Inst. Corp.
MA-61005-CY	b, e	10	5.2×10^4	0.8 ma, d-c	2600	1024-0160
MA-61401-	b	14	7×10^4	b	b	
MA-61405-CY	b, e	14	3.5×10^4	1.6 ma, d-c	1500	Diehl Mfg. Co.
SA-60014-B1		14	3.5×10^4	0.5 v, a-c	1000	FPE25-11
SA-60014-A2	g	14	3.5×10^4	0.5 v, a-c	1000	
MA-1501		50	5×10^4	1 v, a-c	1000	Diehl
MA-1511		50	5×10^4	1 ma, d-c	1000	Mfg. Co.
ST-65011-DY	b	50	13.7	25 ma, d-c	6500	FPF49-9
MA-1601		175	2×10^4	1.5 v, a-c	1000	
MA-1611		175	3×10^5	2 ma, d-c	250	Diehl
MA-617562-DY	b	175	100	17 ma, d-c	5000	Mfg. Co.
MA-617522-DY	b	175	100	17 ma, d-c	5000	FPF85-18-1
MA-617540-CY	b	175	150	60 ma, d-c	400	
MA-1701		650	6.4×10^5	1 v, a-c	1000	
MA-1711		650	1×10^6	1.5 ma, d-c	350	Diehl Mfg. Co.
SR-675011-DY	b, f	750	32	100 ma, d-c	2400	ZP105-2212-1
SM-675011-DY	b	750	32	100 ma, d-c	2500	
SM-61500011-DY	b	1900	200	60 ma, d-c	2500	Diehl Mfg. Co.
SR-615240-DY	b, f	2000	200	100 ma, d-c	2500	ZP143-2247-1

[*] See notes, p. 220.

Table 13-2. 400-cps Magnetic Amplifiers*

Supply voltage: 115 volts[a]
Output voltage: 115 volts, a-c phase reversible[b]

Model number	Notes	Output (watts)	Maximum power gain[c]	Signal required for full power output	Input impedance (ohms)[c]	Typical motor load[d] Manufacturer and type number
MA-40501-	b	5	4×10^5	b	b	
ST-400611-DY	b	6	35	8 ma, d-c	3300	BuOrd Mark 7
ST-400612-DY	b	6	65	4 ma, d-c	4000	
SM-400620-DW	b	6	78	4.5 ma, d-c	3800	Kollsman Inst. Corp. 1623-0410110-0
MA-41001-	b	10	6×10^5	b	b	
MA-41005-CY	b, e	10	4×10^5	0.50 ma, d-c	900	BuOrd Mark 8
ST-401010-DY	b	10	40	8 ma, d-c	3900	
MA-41501-	b	15	7.8×10^5	b	b	
MA-41505-CY	b, e	15	3.9×10^5	0.55 ma, d-c	1200	Kearfott Co., Inc. R112
ST-401810-DY	b	18	30	8 ma, d-c	5000	
MA-42001-	b	20	8.4×10^5	b	b	
MA-42005-CY	b, e	20	4×10^5	0.55 ma, d-c	1800	
ST-44011-DZ	b	37	17.5	36 ma, d-c	1600	Bendix CK-3000
MA-405003-CY	b	50	1×10^4	1.75 ma, d-c	800	
MA-405002-CX	b	50	1×10^4	1.75 ma, d-c	800	
SR-410020-DX	b, f	90	80	15 ma, d-c	5000	

* See notes, p. 220.

Notes for Tables 13-1 and 13-2:

a. Magnetic amplifiers for other supply voltages can be furnished.

b. The capital letters following the base model number denote input and output characteristics as per table below. Where the letters after the hyphen are omitted the amplifiers can be supplied with any combination of input and output characteristics as per table.

Designation	Approx. input resistance-series connected (Two equal input windings are supplied.) (ohms)	Sensitivity d-c milliamperes for full power output (series-connected)	Designation	Maximum output voltage (Output is electrically isolated.)	Example 400 cps	Example 60 cps
A	1-9	4-8	Z	220	A 400-cps 10-watt model with an input resistance of 450 ohms and a maximum output voltage of 115 volts is designated: MA-41001-CY	A 60-cps 10-watt model with an input resistance of 3000 ohms and a maximum output voltage of 115 volts is designated: MA-61001-CY
B	10-299	2-4	Y	115		
C	300-3000	0.3-0.6	X	67		
K	special	—	W	26		
			S	special		

c. Without external forcing resistor.

d. For space reasons, only one typical motor is listed; any equivalent motor may be used. The magnetic amplifiers are designed to work with all motors within their power rating, although servo performance may vary somewhat with motor used.

e. Three input windings are provided. The data given is for windings on e and two connected in series.

f. Saturable reactors, a-c output voltage, not phase reversible.

g. 1- and 36-speed servo amplifier; self-contained crossover network.

TABLE 13-3.   Fast-response Magnetic Amplifiers

Catalog number	Single-phase supply voltage and frequency	Rated power output	Rated voltage output	Signal req'd for full output with 10,000 ohms input impedance (a-c or d-c)	Signal req'd for full output with 1000 ohms input impedance (a-c or d-c)	Typical motor load	Time of response*
MAF-1	115 v/60 cps	13 watts	110 v a-c phase rev.	1 v		Diehl FPE 25-11	2 cycles
MAF-6	{115 v/400 cps	5 watts	57.5 v a-c phase rev.	1.2 v	0.4 v	Kearfott R110-2	2 cycles
	{115 v/400 cps	10 watts	57.5 v a-c phase rev.	1.6 v	0.6 v	Kearfott R111-2	2 cycles
MAF-7	115 v/400 cps	15 watts	57.5 v a-c phase rev.	2.5 v	1.0 v	Kearfott R112-2	2 cycles

* Measured in cycles of supply frequency necessary to obtain 100% response.

Notes: (1) Transistor or vacuum-tube preamplifiers can be used ahead of the magnetic amplifier if a higher gain is desired.
(2) The MAF-6 and MAF-7 are hermetically sealed.
(3) The MAF-1 is furnished with a separate supply transformer.

TABLE 13-4. Push-pull Magnetic Amplifiers

Catalog number	Single-phase supply voltage and frequency	Rated power output	Rated voltage output	Signal req'd for full output	Typical motor load	Time of response*				Total res. of control windings
						on ($R_s = 0$)	off ($R_s = 0$)	on ($R_s = 20$ K)	off ($R_s = 20$ K)	
MAP-1	115 v/60 cps	5 watts	115 v a-c phase rev.	1.2 ma d-c	Kollsman 951-0160	15 cps	60 cps	4 cps	8 cps	1240 ohms
MAP-2	115 v/60 cps	15 watts	115 v a-c phase rev.	1.6 ma d-c	Diehl FPE 25-11	12 cps	17 cps	7 cps	7 cps	2400 ohms
MAP-3	115 v/60 cps	50 watts	115 v a-c phase rev.	2.0 ma d-c	Diehl FPF 49-9	1-2 sec	3-4 sec	6 cps	11 cps	500 ohms
MAP-3-1	115 v/60 cps	50 watts	115 v a-c phase rev.	7.0 ma d-c	Diehl FPF 49-9	1.3 sec	1.7 sec	5 cps	20 cps	2900 ohms
MAP-4	115 v/60 cps	175 watts	115 v a-c phase rev.	8.0 ma d-c	Diehl FPF 85-18-1	17 cps	66 cps	5 cps	40 cps	6000 ohms
MAP-7	115 v/400 cps	15 watts	115 v a-c phase rev.	0.6 ma d-c	Kearfott R112-2	0.75 sec	2 sec	5 cps	15 cps	2800 ohms
MAP-8	115 v/400 cps	50 watts	110 v a-c phase rev.	1.75 ma d-c	Bendix CK 3000-1-A	45 cps	60 cps	9 cps	12 cps	600 ohms

*Measured in cycles of supply frequency necessary to obtain 63% (on) or 37% (off) of steady-state output in response to a d-c step input.

Notes: (1) Magnetic amplifiers MAP-1, 2, 3, 3-1, 4, and 8 are furnished with separate supply transformers.
(2) R_s = forcing resistor in series with the control winding.
(3) MAP-4 supplied in open type construction unless otherwise specified.

TABLE 13-5. Single-ended Magnetic Amplifiers

Catalog number	Single-phase supply voltage and frequency	Rated power output	Rated voltage output	Load resistance for max. power output	Control signal req'd for full output	Bias signal req'd for min. output	Time of response* on (R_s = 5 K)	off	Resistance of control winding	Resistance of bias winding
MAO-1	115 v/60 cps	4.5 watts	130 v a-c	3800 ohms	3.0 ma d-c	1.0 ma d-c	3 cps	8 cps	1,200 ohms	1,200 ohms
MAO-2	115 v/60 cps	20 watts	120 v a-c	700 ohms	1.8 ma d-c	0.7 ma d-c	3 cps	19 cps	1,300 ohms	1,350 ohms
MAO-4	115 v/60 cps	400 watts	100 v a-c	25 ohms	9.0 ma d-c	1.6 ma d-c	9 cps	25 cps	10,000 ohms	10,000 ohms
MAO-5	115 v/60 cps	575 watts	120 v a-c	25 ohms	6.0 ma d-c	2.7 ma d-c	15 cps	90 cps	10,000 ohms	10,000 ohms

* Measured in cycles of supply frequency necessary to obtain 63% (on) or 37% (off) of steady-state output in response to a d-c step input.

Notes: (1) MAO-4 and MAO-5 supplied in open type construction unless otherwise specified.
(2) MAO-5 is furnished with separate supply transformer.
(3) R_s = forcing resistor in series with the control winding.

Appendices

Appendix A
MAGNETIC AMPLIFIER NOTATION

A	Core cross-sectional area
B	(1) Lines of magnetic force
	(2) Magnetic flux density
	(3) Feedback factor
B_i	Internal flux density
B_s	Saturation flux density
d	Distance between magnetic poles
E	Induced electromotive force
E_C	Control voltage
E_M	Maximum (rectified) average output voltage
E_m	Supply voltage maximum value
F	(1) Force of attraction or repulsion
	(2) Magnetomotive force
f	Frequency of the a-c supply voltage
H	Magnetizing force or magnetic intensity
I	Current
I_B	Current in the bias winding
I_C	Current in the control winding
I_F	Current in the feedback winding
I_L	Current in the load winding
I_{L0}	Quiescent or standing current
K_E	Voltage gain
K_I	Current gain
K_P	Power gain (average output)
K_P'	Power gain (rms output)
k	Coefficient of coupling
k_f	Form factor of output current (equals I_L rms/I_L av)
L	Inductance
L_C	Inductance of the control winding
M	Mutual inductance
m	Magnetic pole strength
μ	Permeability of a medium

μ_v	Permeability of vacuum
N	(1) Number of turns in a conductor
	(2) Number of conductors
N_B	Number of turns in the bias winding
N_C	Number of turns in the control (input) winding
N_F	Number of turns in the feedback winding
NI	Ampere turns
N_L	Number of turns in the load (output) winding
Φ	Magnetic flux
P	Permeance
P_C	Control power
$\mathcal{R}$	Reluctance
$R_{\text{a-c}}$	A-c resistance of the load winding
R_C	Resistance of the control circuit
R_L	Load resistance
SR	Dry-disc rectifier
SX	Saturable reactor
T	Time constant
t	Time
X_L	Inductive reactance
Z	Impedance

Appendix B

FORMULAS*

Saturable Reactors with No Feedback

Character-istic	Series-connected saturable reactor (Fig. B1)	Parallel-connected saturable reactor (Fig. B2)
Control ampere turns	$N_C I_C = I_L N_L$	$N_C I_C = \dfrac{I_L N_L}{2}$
Control current	$I_C = \dfrac{I_L N_L}{N_C}$	$I_C = \dfrac{I_L N_L}{2 N_C}$
Control voltage	$E_C = \dfrac{I_L N_L}{N_C} R_C$	$E_C = \dfrac{I_L N_L}{2 N_C} R_C$
Control power	$P_C = \left(\dfrac{I_L N_L}{N_C}\right)^2 R_C$	$P_C = \left(\dfrac{I_L N_L}{2 N_C}\right)^2 R_C$
Time constant,† seconds	$T = \dfrac{1}{4 f} \dfrac{R_L}{R_C} \dfrac{N_C^2}{N_L^2}$	$T = \dfrac{1}{f} \dfrac{R_L}{N_L^2} \left(\dfrac{N_C^2}{R_C} + \dfrac{N_L^2}{R_{\text{a-c}}}\right)$
Voltage gain	$K_E = \dfrac{I_L R_L}{I_C R_C} = \dfrac{N_C R_L}{N_L R_C}$	$K_E = \dfrac{I_L R_L}{I_C R_C} = \dfrac{2 N_C R_L}{N_L R_C}$
Current gain	$K_I = \dfrac{I_L}{I_C} = \dfrac{N_C}{N_L}$	$K_I = \dfrac{I_L}{I_C} = \dfrac{2 N_C}{N_L}$
Power gain (average output)	$K_P = K_E K_I = \dfrac{N_C^2}{N_L^2} \dfrac{R_L}{R_C}$	$K_P = K_E K_I = 4 \left(\dfrac{N_C}{N_L}\right)^2 \dfrac{R_L}{R_C}$
Power gain†† (rms output)	$K_P' = K_E K_I k_f^2 = k_f^2 \left(\dfrac{N_C}{N_L}\right)^2 \dfrac{R_L}{R_C}$	$K_P' = K_E K_I k_f^2 = 4 k_f^2 \left(\dfrac{N_C}{N_L}\right)^2 \dfrac{R_L}{R_C}$
Maximum (rectified) average output voltage	$E_M = \dfrac{2 E_m}{\pi}$	$E_M = \dfrac{2 E_m}{\pi}$
Maximum output current	$I_L \text{ max} = \dfrac{2}{\pi} \dfrac{E_m}{R_L}$	$I_L \text{ max} = \dfrac{2}{\pi} \dfrac{E_m}{R_L}$

* Compiled by W. J. Dornhoefer and V. H. Krummenacher for *Electrical Manufacturing Design Compendium No. 1A*, 1953.

† Does not include residual delay.

†† k_f = form factor of output current = I_L (rms)/I_L (av).

Saturable Reactors with No Feedback (cont.)

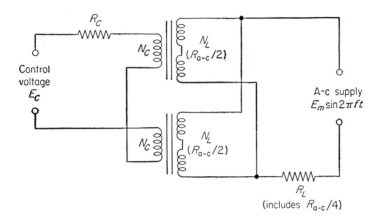

Fig. B1. Non-feedback saturable reactors with series-connected load windings. *Note:* In all cases, R_C includes the resistance of both the control windings and the external circuit, and R_L includes the resistance of the output windings.

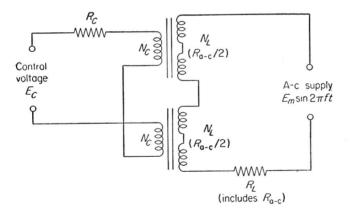

Fig. B2. Non-feedback saturable reactors with parallel-connected load windings.

Magnetic Amplifiers with External Feedback

Characteristic	Series-connected magnetic amplifier (Fig. B3)	Parallel-connected magnetic amplifier (Fig. B4)
Control ampere turns	$N_C I_C = (1 - B) N_L I_L$	$N_C I_C = (1 - B) \dfrac{N_L I_L}{2}$
Control current	$I_C = (1 - B) \dfrac{N_L I_L}{N_C}$	$I_C = (1 - B) \dfrac{N_L I_L}{2 N_C}$
Control voltage	$E_C = (1 - B) \dfrac{N_L I_L}{N_C} R_C$	$E_C = (1 - B) \dfrac{N_L I_L}{2 N_C} R_C$
Control power	$P_C = (1 - B)^2 \left(\dfrac{N_L I_L}{N_C} \right)^2 R_C$	$P_C = (1 - B)^2 \left(\dfrac{N_L I_L}{2 N_C} \right)^2 R_C$
Time constant,† seconds	$T = \dfrac{1}{(1 - B)} \dfrac{R_L}{4 f N_L^2} \left(\dfrac{N_C^2}{R_C} + \dfrac{N_F^2}{R_F} \right)$	$T = \dfrac{1}{(1 - B)} \dfrac{R_L}{f N_L^2} \left(\dfrac{N_C^2}{R_C} + \dfrac{N_F^2}{R_F} + \dfrac{N_L^2}{R_{\text{a-c}}} \right)$
Voltage gain	$K_E = \dfrac{I_L R_L}{I_C R_C} = \dfrac{1}{(1 - B)} \dfrac{N_C R_L}{N_L R_C}$	$K_E = \dfrac{2}{(1 - B)} \dfrac{N_C R_L}{N_L R_C}$
Current gain	$K_I = \dfrac{I_L}{I_C} = \dfrac{1}{(1 - B)} \dfrac{N_C}{N_L}$	$K_I = \dfrac{2}{(1 - B)} \dfrac{N_C}{N_L}$
Power gain (average output)	$K_P = \dfrac{1}{(1 - B)^2} \left(\dfrac{N_C}{N_L} \right)^2 \dfrac{R_L}{R_C}$	$K_P = \dfrac{4}{(1 - B)^2} \left(\dfrac{N_C}{N_L} \right)^2 \dfrac{R_L}{R_C}$
Power gain†† (rms output)	$K_P' = \dfrac{K_f^2}{(1 - B)^2} \left(\dfrac{N_C}{N_L} \right)^2 \dfrac{R_L}{R_C}$	$K_P' = \dfrac{4 K_f^2}{(1 - B)^2} \left(\dfrac{N_C}{N_L} \right)^2 \dfrac{R_L}{R_C}$
Maximum (rectified) average output voltage	$E_M = \dfrac{2 E_m}{\pi}$	$E_M = \dfrac{2 E_m}{\pi}$
Maximum output current	$I_L \max = \dfrac{2 E_m}{\pi R_L}$	$I_L \max = \dfrac{2 E_m}{\pi R_L}$

† Does not include residual delay.
†† k_f = form factor of output current.

Magnetic Amplifiers with External Feedback (cont.)

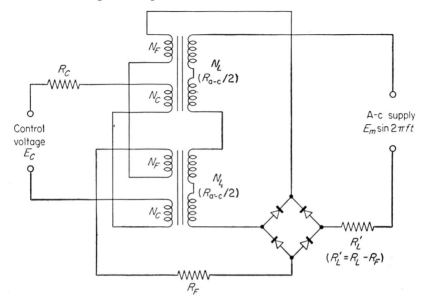

Fig. B3. Magnetic amplifier with external feedback and series-connected load windings. *Note:* $B = N_F/N_L$.

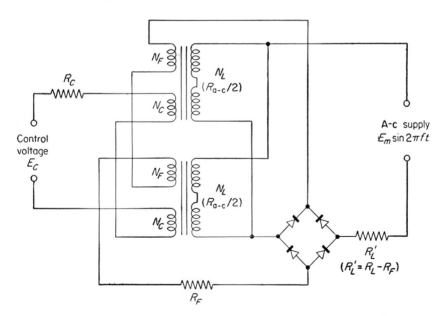

Fig. B4. Magnetic amplifier with external feedback and parallel-connected load windings. *Note:* $B = 2N_F/N_L$.

Magnetic Amplifiers with Internal Feedback

Character-istic	Single-phase magnetic amplifier (Fig. B5)	Three-phase magnetic amplifier (Fig. B6)
Control ampere turns	$N_C I_C = (NI) = NI/\text{inch} \times L_C$	$N_C I_C = (NI) = NI/\text{inch} \times L_C$
Control current	$I_C = \dfrac{(NI)}{N_C}$	$I_C = \dfrac{(NI)}{N_C}$
Control voltage	$E_C = NI \dfrac{R_C}{N_C}$	$E_C = NI \dfrac{R_C}{N_C}$
Control power	$P_C = NI^2 \dfrac{R_C}{N_C^2}$	$P_C = NI^2 \dfrac{R_C}{N_C^2}$
Time constant, seconds	$T = \dfrac{1}{2f} \dfrac{K_E N_C}{N_L}$	$T = \dfrac{1}{3f} \dfrac{K_E N_C}{N_L}$
Voltage gain	$K_E = \dfrac{E_M N_C}{NIR_C}$	$K_E = \dfrac{E_M N_C}{NIR_C}$
Current gain	$K_I = \dfrac{E_M N_C}{NIR_L}$	$K_I = \dfrac{E_M N_C}{NIR_L}$
Power gain	$K_P = \dfrac{E_M^2 N_C^2}{(NI)^2 R_L R_C}$	$K_P = \dfrac{E_M^2 N_C^2}{(NI)^2 R_L R_C}$
Maximum (rectified) average output voltage	$E_M = \dfrac{2}{\pi} E_m \left(\dfrac{2N\Phi f}{2N\Phi_f + N\Phi_\Delta} \right)$	$E_M = \dfrac{3}{\pi} E_m \left(\dfrac{2N\Phi f}{2N\Phi f + N\Phi_\Delta} \right)$
Maximum output current	$I_L \max = \dfrac{2}{\pi} \dfrac{E_m}{R_L} \left(\dfrac{2N\Phi f}{2N\Phi f + N\Phi_\Delta} \right)$	$I_L \max = \dfrac{3}{\pi} \dfrac{E_m}{R_L} \left(\dfrac{2N\Phi f}{2N\Phi f + N\Phi_\Delta} \right)$

Magnetic Amplifiers with Internal Feedback (cont.)

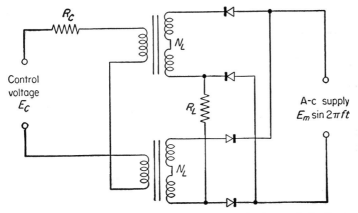

Fig. B5. Single-phase magnetic amplifier with internal feedback.

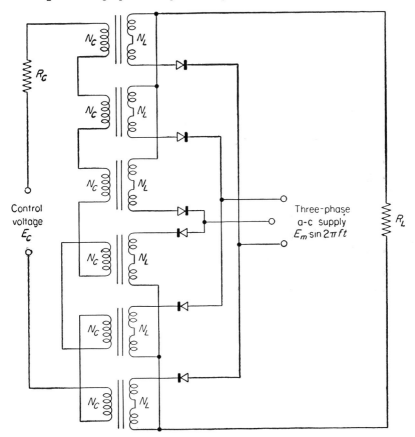

Fig. B6. Three-phase magnetic amplifier with internal feedback.

Appendix C
ANSWERS TO REVIEW QUESTIONS

2.1. (a) 10 dynes
(b) Force of attraction
(c) 250 dynes
2.2. 7.6 centimeters
2.4. 20,000 gausses

3.1. (a) 500 ampere turns
(b) 1 ampere
3.2. 5.024 gilberts
3.3. 6.28 oersteds
3.4. 5 kilogausses
3.5. 25 square centimeters
3.6. 1.333
3.7. 312,500 gausses
3.8. 160 volts
3.10. (*Hint:* solve for the area first; $A = \pi d^2/4$, where d is the diameter of a circle.) 2600 microhenries
3.11. (a) 157,000 ohms
(b) 127 microamperes

4.1. 103 volts
4.3. (a) 0.08 second
(b) 350 ohms

6.1. 8
6.2. Quadrupled
6.3. 3600

8.2. 4444
8.3. 7500

Index

A

A-c controlled feedback, 152–153
A-c voltage regulation, 195–198
Alexanderson, E. F. W., 6
Amplidyne, control characteristic of, 4–5
Amplifier, types of, 1–2
Annealing, 45
Audio amplification, 207–208
Autopilots, 6

B

Battery charging control, 92–93
B-H curve:
  defined, 2–3, 37–39
  idealized forms of, 62–63
  in saturable reactor, 61–66
  rectangular, 43–44
Bias:
  in external feedback amplifier, 140–145
  in internal feedback amplifier, 163
Bridge magnetic amplifier, 159–161
Burgess, C. F., 6

C

Cascaded magnetic amplifiers, 110–111
Coefficient of coupling, 52
Coercive field (force), 40
Compensation for quiescent
  current, 111–114
Compound feedback magnetic
  amplifier, 163–164
Constrained magnetization, 77–80
Control characteristics:
  amplidyne, 4–5
  magnetic amplifier, 4–5
  saturable reactor, 87
  thyratron, 4–5

Control of d-c motor speed, 122–125
Control of servo motor, 129–130
Control response of saturable reactor, 84–86
Control windings, 1–2, 76–77
Core:
  construction, 74–76
  materials, 44
  permeability, 2
Coulomb's law, 20
Counterpoise, 112
Critical atomic distance, 28
Current and voltage relationships,
  saturable reactor, 77-84
Current transformer equivalency, 77–78

D

D-c magnetic amplifiers, 200–201
Diamagnetic materials, 23–24
Dimmer, 202–204
Discriminator, 132–133
Domains, 28–29
Doubler magnetic amplifier, 158–161
Dry-disc rectifiers, 7

E

Eddy-current loss, 43
Educational magnetic amplifiers, 188–195
EI rectangular lamination, 75–76
Electric and magnetic circuits,
  comparison of, 36–37
Electric furnace control, 90–91
Electrodynamometer, 113
Electromagnet, 33
Electromagnetic induction, 46–47
Exchange forces between atoms, 28
External (extrinsic) feedback
  circuit, 135–147

F

Faraday, M., 19
Faraday's experiments, 46–47
Feedback:
    a-c controlled, 152–153
    external (extrinsic), 102, 135–153
    internal (intrinsic), 102, 155–171
    magnetic amplifier, 3
Feedback amplifier, gain of, 137–139
Ferromagnetic materials:
    classification of, 23–24
    power losses in, 42–43
Figure of merit, 138
Flux, magnetic (*see* Magnetic flux)
Flux density:
    defined, 34–35
    initial, 39
    residual, 40
    saturation, 44
    variations in B-H curve, 63–66
Flux detectors, 169–170
Forced magnetization, 77–80
Four-reactor magnetic
    amplifier, 150–151, 166–167
Frankenfeld, B., 6
Full-wave magnetic amplifier, 159–161

G

Gauss (unit), 22, 34
Generator voltage regulation, 125–126
Gilbert, W., 19
Gilbert (unit), 33
Guided missiles, 6

H

Half-wave push-pull magnetic
    amplifier, 161–163
Harmonic amplifier circuits, 130–132
Henry, J., 19
Henry (unit), 49
High-frequency saturable reactors, 204–205
High-speed magnetic servo
    amplifier, 183–186
Hysteresis:
    effect, 29
    defined, 39–42
    loops, rectangular, 6–7
    losses, 42

I

Impedance, 51

Induced electromotive force,
    direction of, 47–48
Inductance, 48–50
Induction:
    electromagnetic, 46–47
    magnetic, 26
    mutual, 51–52
    self, 48–50
Inductive reactance, 50–51
Internal (intrinsic) feedback,
    135–136, 155–171

L

Lamination, 43, 75–76
Left-hand rule:
    conductor, 31
    solenoid, 32–33
Lenz's law, 47–48
Lines of magnetic force (inductive):
    characteristics of, 21–22
    defined, 21
Load lines, 105–108
Load windings, 1–2, 82–84
Lodestone, 18
Low-power instrument servo system,
    177-179

M

Magnetic amplifier:
    advantages, 2, 211–213
    alloys used in, 44
    applications of, 122–133, 195–209
    balanced push-pull, 116–119
    basic, 103–105
    bias in, 145–147
    bridge, 160–161
    cascaded, 110–111
    characteristics of, 210–223
    compensating circuits for, 111–114
    compound feedback, 163–164
    control characteristics, 4–5
    core materials, 44
    disadvantages of, 211–213
    discriminator, 132–133
    doubler, 158–161
    educational, 188–195
    external (extrinsic) feedback, 140–145
    feedback applications of, 156
    feedback in, 135–136
    flux detectors, 169–170
    formulas, 228–233

Magnetic amplifier (*cont.*):
  four-reactor, 166–167
  full-wave, 159–161
  fundamentals of operation, 2–4
  half-wave, 161–163
  history of, 6–7
  internal (intrinsic) feedback in, 155–171
  load lines, 105–108
  multistage, 165
  nonpolarized, 104
  notation, 226–227
  operating limits, 106
  output characteristics, 108–109
  packaged, 2
  polarity-sensitive, 114–116
  polarized, 104
  power gain, 119–120
  properties of, 210–223
  push-pull, 116–119, 147–151, 161–163
  rating specifications, 215–217
  regenerative feedback, 139–140
  reliability of, 6
  remote control positioning, 170–171
  servomechanism applications, 173–186
  significant patents, 7–15
  snap action in, 151–152
  three-phase, 167–168
  transfer characteristics, 108–109
  two-reactor internal feedback, 158–163
  uncompensated, 111
  variable-gain, 120-121
Magnetic and electric circuits,
  comparison of, 36–37
Magnetic axis, 19
Magnetic effects of current, 30–31
Magnetic field:
  around conductor, 30–31
  around solenoid, 32–33
  definition of, 21
  of earth, 22
Magnetic flux, 22, 33–34
Magnetic induction, 26
Magnetic intensity, 34
Magnetic materials, classification of, 22–24
Magnetic mines, 6
Magnetic poles:
  Coulomb's law for, 20
  forces between, 20
  north and south, 19, 22
Magnetic reference standard, 209
Magnetic servo amplifiers, 182–183
Magnetic units, 36

Magnetism:
  history of, 18–19
  introduction to, 17–18
  relationship to electricity, **17**
Magnetization curve (*see B-H* **curve**)
Magnetizing force, 34
Magnetomotive force, 33
Magnetostriction, 29
Maxwell (unit), 22, 34
Measurement, d-c and oscillographic,
  94–97
Medium-power positioning servo
  system, 175–177
Molecular theory of magnetism, **24–27**
Mutual induction, 51–52

N

Natural magnetization, 80–81
Nonpolarized magnetic amplifiers, 104

O

Oersted, H. C., 19
Oersted (unit), 34
Ohm's law, 34
Output characteristics of magnetic
  amplifier, 108–109

P

Paramagnetic materials, 23
Permeability, 20, 35, 38, 39
Permeance, 35–36
Phase-sensitive demodulator, 177
Phase shifting, using saturable reactor,
  93–94
Polarity-sensitive:
  magnetic amplifier, **114–116**
  saturable reactor, 97–100
Polarized magnetic amplifier, 104
Power gains in magnetic amplifiers,
  119-120
Power losses in cores, 42-43
Power supply voltage regulation, 198-200
Push-pull magnetic amplifier, 116–119,
  147–151, 161–163

Q

Quiescent (*Q*) current, 109

R

Reactance, inductive, 50–51
Rectangular cores. 74–76

Regenerative feedback amplifier:
  introduction to, 135
  operation of, 139–140
  snap action in, 151–152
Regulating a d-c generator, 206–207
Reluctance, 35-36
Remote control positioning, 170–171
Reset magnetic amplifier, 183–186
Resonant control circuits, 100–101
Retentivity, 40
Ring cores, 74–75
Rolling, 45–46

S

Saturable-core reactor (*see* Saturable
  reactor)
Saturable reactor:
  applications of, 87–101
  basic circuits, 66–69
  battery charging application, 92–93
  characteristics of, 62–66
  control response, 84–86
  core construction, 74–76
  current and voltage relationships, 77–84
  d-c measurement application, 94–97
  defined, 54
  disadvantages of basic circuit, 67
  electric furnace control, 90–91
  forced magnetization, 77–80
  function of, 60–61
  fundamental, 6, 54–62
  high-frequency, 204–205
  load limitation, 82
  magnetic leakage in, 72–74
  multiple control windings, 76–77
  natural magnetization, 80–81
  operation of, 56–60
  oscillograph measurement application,
    94–97
  parallel a-c coils on, 71–72
  permeability variations in, 59
  phase-shifting applications of, 93–94
  polarity-sensitive, 97–99
  resonant control circuits, 100–101
  series-opposing control winding, 67–68
  split core in, 73–74
  theatre lighting control application,
    88–90
  three-legged, 55–56, 69–72
  three-phase, 76

Saturable reactor (*cont.*):
  time constant, 84–86
  time response of, 71–72
  twin core, 68–69
  uses of, 61, 66–67
  windings, 54–55
Saturation curve (*see* B-H curve)
Self-induction, 48–50
Self-saturated feedback, 136–155
Semiconductor amplifier, 1
Servomechanism applications, 173–186
Servo motor, control of, 129–130
Snap action, 151–152
Solenoid, magnetic field about, 32–33
Spinning electrons, 27
Spiral cores, 74–76
Stacked cores, 74–76
Standing current, 109
Suppressed even-harmonic currents, 79
Synchro signal adapter servo system,
    179-181

T

Temperature control, 126–129, 207
Theatre-light control, 88–90
Theories of magnetism, 24–29
Three-legged saturable reactor (*see*
    Saturable reactor)
Three-phase magnetic amplifier (*see*
    Magnetic amplifier)
Thyratron, control characteristics of, 4–5
Thyratron grid control, 93–94
Time constant of saturable reactor, 84–86
Toroids, 74–75
Torque motor servo system, 182
Transfer characteristics of magnetic
    amplifier, 108–109, 115
Transistor amplifier, 1
Two-phase servo motor, control of, 129–130
Two-reactor internal-feedback
    amplifier, 158–163

U

UI rectangular lamination, 75–76
Units, systems of, 36

V

Variable-gain magnetic amplifier, 120–121
Voltage regulation, generator, 125–126